PRAISE FOR WINNING TEAMS WORKBOOK

"Creating an effective and cohesive team takes a great deal of skill, patience, persistence and the ability to motivate people to all move in the same direction. One of the key skill sets needed today is that of situational leadership; recognizing both the circumstances and the necessary tools needed to move a team towards high performance based on existing conditions. This book combines both the art and current science of team building that will enable the reader to develop the right strategies for their team to become a forward thinking, innovative and successful team. I highly recommend this book!"

– Dr. Michael Mittelman,
President at SALUS University,
(Former) Deputy Surgeon General of the U.S. Navy

"How Teams are supported and led clearly affects their performance. Winning Teams Workbook provides the tools needed to analyze the present state of personal development, team health and organizational well-being and make appropriate changes. Creating and developing winning teams is still more art than science, but this book provides the latest thinking about the variables involved and how to arrange them for maximum efficiency and effectiveness."

– Tia McLaurin,
Google, 2020 40 under 40

If I had written a book, the concepts, guidance, motivation and sheer power of this work is what I would have wanted to create. The Winning Teams Workbook is sheer genius that recognizes the unique significance of "peopling" as the differentiating formula in the workforce. It provides powerful strategies that can be executed in straightforward ways with approaches, techniques, and the tools to be employed by any winning team (burgeoning, or already developed - mature or maturing). This work guides leadership activities to address every protocol, formula, discipline, and strategy that is significant to their Return on Effectiveness (ROE) and bottom line success."

– Gilda Stafford
Human Dynamics Leader

If you desire to become a better leader or build a leadership culture within your organizations then you must add Dr. Magee's "Winning Teams Workbook: Taking Teams From Average to Extraordinary" to your organization's leadership toolkit. The thought leadership and corresponding exercises will drive individual and collective results within your team and your organizations.

– Stephanie A. Parson, Ph.D.,
President, Crowned Grace International

"Having read "Winning Teams", I know that I will forever embrace and encourage Ki's powerful three-point model for success, "I win, I make sure you win, and we all win"! Layered with solid advice and practical tools for application, this engaging, uplifting and well researched workbook is a must have for any leader who wants to grow teams, families, or communities with authenticity and integrity. "Winning Teams", is indeed a fresh take and a welcome addition to the leadership performance genre."

– Sandy Lewis, CEO,
Positive Shift Coaching

"Ki walks her talk. While it would have been more than enough to share the wealth of self, team and organizational development perspectives she carefully lays out for us, she goes further. She makes sure YOU WIN by backing up the information with solid exercises and activities that support real change. If you then use it to go out and bring change to the world, WE WIN, and clearly this is what Ki intends."

– Liz Garrett, Author,
"*The Opposite of Burnout*" and "*Intentionology*"

WINNING TEAMS

WORKBOOK

TAKING TEAMS FROM AVERAGE TO EXCEPTIONAL

DR. SHEKINAH "KI" MAGEE

For more information and for bulk orders, contact: Ki@KiCanHelp.com

First Edition: January 2022 ISBN: 978-1-7371149-0-1

Published by Clear And Present Executive Coaching and Consulting Services, LLC in Washington, DC.

A Gift from Ki....

Now that you have your copy of **Winning Teams Workbook: Taking Teams from Average to Exceptional**, you are on your way to higher performance and unprecedented achievement, connectedness, and impact! Plus, your Customers, Teams, and entire Organization will obtain extraordinary benefits, as well.

You'll also receive the special bonus I created to add to your toolkit ... **The Winning Teams Field Guide**, which contains downloadable templates, assessments, and activity guides, along with additional instructions and my tips from various client implementations.

There's so much confusing information out there about how to take teams from average to exceptional and how to create, build, and sustain an organizational culture where these teams thrive and flourish. When you finish this book, you'll be armed with what you need to know to Win, make sure Others Win, so Everyone Wins!!!

While **The Winning Teams Field Guide** is offered for sale, as a special bonus, you can claim it for free here:

https://WinningTeamsWorkbook.com/guide

The sooner you know how to take teams from average to exceptional, the better your chances for improving your employees' and customers' experience and improving your entire organization.

I'm in your corner. Let me know if I can help further.

Here's to Winning Teams!

Best,

Shekinah "Ki" Magee

DEDICATION

To my amazing husband, Gerald, whose love and support encouraged me to undertake this project and whose patience and encouragement allowed me to finish.

To my incredible parents, Nathaniel (Charles) and Teresa, who taught me that if I work hard enough, assert myself, and use my mind and imagination, I can shape the world to my desires.

To my Grandmother, Lillie, the most brilliant leader I know, and the Matriarch of our large and loving family.

Acknowledgments

A most heartfelt "Thank You" to all the teams I have had the honor to serve and lead, and to the countless leaders who work tirelessly, day in and day out, to create environments where winning teams can exist and be successful. Your stories, lessons, challenges, and triumphs inspire this book and my work, every day.

I hope to make you proud.

NOTE TO THE READER

Winning Teams Are More Important Today Than Ever Before

We spend eight, and sometimes twelve or more hours a day with our leaders and team members. This time is extremely productive and satisfying for some, but miserable and soul-crushing for others. We owe it to each other to work towards the former, while vowing to annihilate the latter. Organizations must create spaces where work enhances lives for all involved: customers, business leaders, and teams.

This Book Will Help Us Shape and Change Our World

Concepts shared here can be applied to work teams, athletic teams, families, religious groups, communities – any instances where a group of people choose to come together to take performance and impact to the next level. And let's face it, we all have a next level.

Start on an Immediate Fix, Then Work On Long-term Solution

This book is organized in a way that supports you with immediate needs – The preface, "Who Says We're Losing?" speaks to the significant risks to organizations that fail to keep pace with innovation, miss out on attracting, engaging, and sustaining current and next generation talent and who regress in their ability to respond effectively to emergent changes.

If you are concerned these may be issues for your organization, there are some immediate fixes suggested in sections related to personal assessment and development (I Win), Support to Others through Intervention and Coaching (I Make Sure You Win), and Organizational (Cultural) Analysis, Design, Shaping and Development (We All Win). Sections also offer long-term planning and strategic approaches to support teams, so they thrive, enjoying heightened levels of performance once on track.

We Can Change The World*

When I was young, I wanted to change the world.

I found it difficult to change the world, so I tried to change my nation.

When I found I could not change my nation, I began to focus on my town. I could not change my town, and as time went on, I tried to change my family.

Today, I realize the only thing I can change is myself, and suddenly I realize that in changing myself, I could have an impact on my family. My family and I could make an impact on our town. The town's impact could change the nation and we could indeed change the world.

*Modified by Author, based on 'I Wanted
to Change the World'
poem by Anonymous

TABLE OF CONTENTS

TABLE OF TOOLS

FOREWORD

Ki and I have been working together for over two years transforming an organizational culture, and we have hard-won experience 'in the trenches.' We've taken groups of independent performers and brought them together for a common purpose, and patched up broken relationships among individual team members, functional areas, and divisions to transform them into deliverers of extraordinary mission and business value. Over this time, I have been impressed by Ki's pragmatic and practical way of engaging teams. Her coaching style is action-oriented and deeply rooted in supporting people through their individual development journey. Her interventions align individual and team development with organizational strategies – benefiting all levels. Ki excels at bringing together professionals of divergent skill sets, experiences, and backgrounds to increase business (mission) effectiveness and impact.

This book is not about formulaic success. Cookie cutter, prescriptive methods do not work for leaders of dynamic, diverse, agile enterprises. And just as organizations and their cultures differ, so do the leaders who lead them – we are each shaped by our values, experiences, successes, and failures. Here is a great analogy: an Auto Mechanic is a "knowledgeable person" without their tools. With their tools, they can fix anything. The «Three Wins» strategy serves to provide awareness of all the untapped potential at one's disposal – asking the right questions to generate thought and challenge assumptions. It represents the tools, and in this case, techniques needed to transform into an extremely accomplished organization.

"Three Wins" asks the right questions. As one who has lived through the process and benefitted from its strategies, methods, and approaches, I can most definitively affirm, it works! Our team grew from one of the most disliked organizations with a reputation of poor customer service to a shining example of best practices and a model for success – a large part of it attributable to the strategies presented here.

Leading in today's world takes a mix of skill, fortitude, a healthy dose of empathy combined with an open mind and acceptance of diverse opinions. Authenticity, integrity, and transparency are the key ingredients. If you lack these qualities, some self-reflection may be in order – this book can help with that. It meets you and your team where you are – whether you are struggling to determine individual development needs for a new role, supporting emergent needs of coaching and evolving others, or being appointed as the responsible steward of ensuring organizational achievement by creating and fostering an environment where all team members and teams can flourish.

Successful leaders will embrace an "I Win" mindset, equipped with confidence and strong self-awareness resulting from an investment in personal development. The work then moves to building trust within teams and maturing them from compliant to committed partners, operating from a space of "I Make Sure You Win." With time, consistent leadership, staying on message, and living your values, your actions become the reinforcing behavior for the wins. That is when "We All Win." My organization's transformation is living proof of it.

– Donald Bauer
Chief Technology Officer,
Office of Technology Services
U. S. Department of State

Preface

Who Says We're Losing?!

At this point, you're probably asking, "Who says we're losing?" and "What was lost?" Those are fair questions. These were the first questions that occurred to me when anticipating possible responses to the introduction of a Winning Teams "Three Win" Philosophy. Another way to pose these questions would be, "Are the issues facing global leaders and organizations today really that different from the routine, expected challenges of the past?"

To this, the answer is a resounding "Yes!" While change and evolution within organizations is a given, the types of changes presenting have been essentially "once in a generation." Additionally, these massive unprecedented changes are occurring within dynamic and ever-changing contexts, driven by daily new discoveries, understandings, and preferences. This leads to a need for broader perspective, increased flexibility, and a breaking away from antiquated assumptions about how people work in organizations.

This is largely because the demographics of the people who work within organizations are changing along with the systems they use, their beliefs about work and roles, and their expectations about the work environment in which they function. Rahschulte (2010) offers that change is inevitable, considering that as one system changes, it impacts another, which in effect forces change in another organization: it's a continuing non-stop ripple. He goes on to present this insight as evidence of a holonic world, a world where all systems are connected to one another, and a world where all systems are living entities, with a constant inclination towards growth. Organizations are remarkably similar to organisms. Culture is the organization's unique personality and its beliefs about what is possible and what is not. Through their culture, organizations experience fears, joys, pains, and triumphs. Culture has a journey, a vision, and a destiny, making them capable of wins and losses.

A quick web-based query of "Is America Losing?" resulted in over two million hits! Each hit provided a sobering look at what was lost: conservative values (Ball, 2015), health care (Fontenot, 2015), military readiness and national security (Fallows, 2015), and its voice (Hyatt, 2013), just to name a few. While it is completely up for debate whether we as a country, society, or planet are losing, most can agree that no one is opposed to the prospect of a win. Most would agree with the sentiments of Jack Kemp: "Winning is like shaving, you either do it every day or wind up looking like a bum."

In an "I win. I make sure YOU win. WE all win!" world, people are not just responsible for their own success; they are wholly and unapologetically responsible for the success of others. And this commitment to another person's success is not passive, it is intentional and deliberate. It means that I commit just as much thought, care, and effort towards my teammates' success as I would to my own. It means my assessment of my own success will be inextricably linked to my ability to make sure my partners, my colleagues, my spouse, my boss, my family, my community—whomever the situation involves—also succeed. I ensure they win or there is no win, which is an implausible and unacceptable outcome because of part one of the philosophy: I win.

Just a little background on Gilda, who introduced me to this concept. She's one of the fiercest, most phenomenal coaches I have ever met. She oozed confidence and charisma. The energy of her presence was that of an executive, but it was light and totally authentic. During that fateful conversation, Gilda shared that she was committed to our success, and how her commitment had nothing to do with the company policies and everything to do with her personal code of behavior. "You see, I win – *and I'm going to win*! You should never trust anyone who says they are not about making sure they win. But I'm also going to make sure you win. That way we all win: the team, the client, and the entire organization."

I can't tell you how awesome it was to hear her say that!! Being new to the organization and not fully knowing what would be expected of me, Gilda received my respect, my commitment, and my loyalty with those few words that I'd never heard spoken from a leader in all my years with the military or in the years that followed in the civilian sector. Her assertion really resonated with me. It outlined a clear and transparent approach to figuring out how we win in organizations. It dismissed old problematic paradigms of winners and losers, or beliefs around the myth of sacrificing certain individuals to serve "the greater good." This was the flavor of excuse I had grown accustomed to managers making, in order to justify initiatives and actions that had not been fully assessed. Gilda's assertions of her "Three Win" Concept led me to ponder the question by which so many ventures into the land of innovation begin: "What if?"

What if I wrote out a game plan to implement the "Three Win" Concept based on philosophies and cases learned from my doctoral studies? What if leaders took a wildly optimistic view of the work and applied it to their work, family, and communities? What if those work teams, family members, and communities applied the workbook's solutions? What is possible? Could we change the world?

This workbook will offer fresh and innovative approaches and much-needed upgrades from the solution sets and tools of the past that are no longer serving organizations or the leaders who love them. To keep pace with the new trends driving change within industries, leaders will want to consider the following three questions:

Dr. Shekinah "Ki" Magee   xxix

Question #1: How Are We Nurturing Innovation?

In a deeply connected system of systems, globally-connected world, every leader is a global leader. Global leaders must have a broadening global perspective. They must take on different beliefs and behaviors than were required to become a successful domestic leader. Cabrera and Unruh (2012) observe that evolving beliefs and behaviors are prerequisites for domestic leaders to bridge the gap towards becoming more globally oriented. The authors note that many Western leaders tend to be guilty of holding and trying to apply domestic-based beliefs and behaviors within a context, which clearly warrants a global perspective instead. They go on to warn global leaders to not become too comfortable with the deeply entrenched thinking of the typical, wealthy Westerner, whose thought processes are fundamentally ethnocentric in nature. They counsel that true global leadership requires an openness to different ideas, innovations, and perspectives.

The authors also identify the need for leaders to develop their global orientation to engage in advanced development practices, such as self-reflection and internal examination. It was this insight that fed the individual learning process and should ultimately answer enterprise leaders' questions around who they are and where they want to go.

Leaders who want to maintain their standing as leaders must see their global leadership role as having missionary-like implications. Missionaries show up as servants to the community. They are service focused, but not subservient. Missionaries operate with openness towards building and letting go because, oftentimes, they will develop close relationships, and then they will one day have to move on to what's next.

Global leaders that are dynamic, innovative, and resourceful are in high demand today. They become accustomed to building, growing, developing, and then moving to the next mission, project, or assignment. These types of leaders do the deep inner work to be more aligned with their principles and values. They see it as crucial to authentically engaging and connecting with people. Leaders must have high self-awareness and a strong sense of self and it is only in this space of personal alignment that leaders can create an environment where individuals feel safe to experiment, thus making room for exploration, innovation, and curiosity.

Fletcher (2013) observes that curiosity is essential to developing successful mind habits which allow individuals to make procedural knowledge—also known as "the How" of a process—more visible. Without this in-depth visibility of the "as is" process, it is almost impossible to come up with an innovative "to be" solution. However, all too often, team members are not made privy to the bigger picture. Even more concerning, in his studies, the author determined that some organizational entities had employed measures to intentionally obscure processes, a practice which many team members found to be highly offensive and distasteful.

This misstep in organizational dynamics has left far too many would-be committed team players stuck in the realm of "cooperative" or simply "compliant" because they felt needlessly confused and lacked clarity related to leader expectations and the role of their fellow teammates. When employees have no information and they are just doing what they have been told to avoid punitive consequences, they are compliant. When team members have some understanding around what they are being asked to do and for what purpose, they tend to lean towards being cooperative. They are more open to partnering and will give the effort the benefit of the doubt. If team members are given the entire big picture–the big "why" driving the activity–and they are informed like key stakeholders, they will act as partners. They will even go so far as to pick up the mantle and see the effort through themselves, if and when the lead initiator is called away. That is commitment. That is what every leader must strive for because they never know when they may be called away to the next assignment, role, or need. Global leaders have a missionary mindset.

In today's global setting, transparency is a virtue. It is better to seek transparency because most partners will demand it. Global leaders must gain comfort creating environments of transparency where they do not already exist. They must enforce the standard, "When in doubt, ask, and if a matter is still unclear, ask another question." Curiosity is a competency that supports accelerated learning within and across disciplines, trades, and professions (Fletcher, 2013). For the purposes of this introduction, a fitting question would be, "If a Three Win Strategy were the answer to the most tenacious challenges of global organizations, what

xxxii   Winning Teams Workbook

would it look like?" This workbook will not only paint that picture, it will also provide practical tools and exercises that any leader can use with their team.

Question #2: How Are We Supporting the Next Generation Leader?

Why introduce a "Three Win" approach right now, when the field of leadership is littered with old and newly emerging viewpoints and opinions? The simple answer can be found by checking the changes in demographics. Even a cursory review will demonstrate that we have a newly emerging generation of leaders unlike any we have ever encountered up to this point. Tung and King (2016) observe that Millennials—those born between the early 1980s to early 2000s, account for a population of eighty million. The men and women who encompass this generation are easily the largest age grouping in American history.

This generation has from a young age witnessed their parents and the world's reactions to 9/11, the dot-com busts, corporate corruption, market crashes, and over a decade of wars in Afghanistan and Iraq. Many experts argue that this highly volatile, violent, and devastating experience made many millennial parents overprotective. These experts assert that millennial parents sheltered their children and encouraged low-risk activities such as video games, which caused many millennials to gravitate towards and develop an affinity with technological advances, making them the first generation to which technology was a native resource. Through the leveraging of technological resources,

Millennials became more mobile, and more versatile, and this drove higher performance in work situations which required high ingenuity, flexibility, and collaboration of efforts.

However, many of the social "soft skills" were left under-developed, making this generation well-known for being both high performance and high maintenance. To engage with them, global leaders will require new approaches that were not needed to engage the work forces of prior generations. This generation has different motivations and they find it harder to trust in big organizational enti-ties, many of which, they learned, were highly corrupt and fragile, based on the observations of their devel-opmental years. As a result, a fair portion of Millennials have trouble trusting the world around them and have instead decided to focus on creating their own lives (Bol-ser and Gosciej, 2015).

In addition to their significant numbers and unique perspec-tive, cultivated by numerous defining moments in Ameri-can history, Millennials are also the most culturally diverse generation ever, with more than 44% identifying as an ethnic or cultural minority and one in five identifying as Hispanic. If companies hope to remain viable and continue to gain mar-ket share amongst increasingly diverse consumer markets and talent pools, they must evaluate their current work-force, market strategy, and company culture to determine if all levels of their business echo the new American identity.

In addition to the changing face of our next generation of leaders, organizations must also consider how this impacts the generations already present. For the first time in history, five generations of workers–the Veterans, the Boomers, Generation X, Millennials, and Generation Z–have graced the workforce. When different generational members collide, they present unique challenges for leaders, whose job it is to bring everyone's talents, energies, and passions together behind a common purpose. All while each generation brings with it its own expectations, values, behaviors, habits, and motivations (Gourani, 2019).

In the past, leaders might have considered these many competing generations and their changing wants and needs, and thought, *We're going to have to make several concessions, a few trade-offs, and numerous compromises which will leave everyone dissatisfied.* However, in a "Three Win" world, leaders can help their teams cultivate personal belief systems that value and welcome the prospect of winning together and invite diverse backgrounds, cultures, genders, beliefs, and experiences to solutions. Moreover, leaders can model and expect others to model the "Three Win" perspective, ensuring not only they win, but that they take others with them into the winner's circle.

Question #3: How Are We Keeping People Engaged?

Whitmore (2013) asserts that over 70% of employees do not use their full talents at work. Evidence of this (in addition to survey responses) can be found by looking at what employees do outside of work and during a crisis; both are examples or incidences where organizations tend to respond in efficient, effective, noble, heroic, and innovative ways. How much better would our organizations, communities, industry, and society be if they could somehow tap into that 30% reserve that team members seldom utilize? If we could just get a 50% increase to an average of 85%, there is no telling what additional possibilities might unfold.

In 2016, Gallup released a study on workplace engagement, which provided great insight into what possibilities rest with a more engaged workforce. Researchers found that when it came to team performance, the organizations that excelled in employee engagement had a 78% higher success rate compared to companies that were in the beginning and developing phases of their employee engagement initiatives. The science is pretty clear: teams with high employee engagement nearly double their odds of success across all business/work units at double the rate of those organizations that are not making employee engagement a priority.

To get the most from the Millennial workforce, leaders will need to recognize the many benefits this newly emerging workforce brings to the table. For example, many are smart, technologically savvy, earnest, and optimistic. While it is important to recognize the emerging generation's workforce, leaders cannot ignore the fact that employees are working longer into old age, and it is paramount that they appreciate how all the generations act and react to one another.

Bolser and Gosciej (2015) assert there is a social exchange gap that must be bridged by all generations, and it is the task of the multi-generational team leader to do so. Social exchange theory asserts that social relationships are created, developed, and destroyed based on perceived benefits to costs calculations. The social exchange theory's conceptual framework can be best leveraged to explain generational development within the generational context.

In a "Three Win" world, leaders welcome this opportunity to bring so many different individuals to the table and introduce them to the principles of Three Wins: "I Win, I Make Sure You Win, That Way We All Win." Teams that possess a "Three Win" mindset win individually, collectively, and frequently, which makes the minor adjustments in perspective well worth any sacrificed, underperforming belief systems.

The Winning Teams Workbook is Here to Help!!

In putting this workbook together, it was my hope to bring about the values of mutual respect, acceptance, and transparency to the forefront. They are essential to the establishment, development, and sustainment of a winning team. This book emerged from my sincere belief that those who will use this workbook confront turbulent times, along with personal and professional conundrums daily. Today's teams meet challenges on an international and global stage while maintaining their own personal communities' clear and identifiable qualities. They are both reflective- and action-oriented. They understand that collaboration is not only important, but vital to achieving effective and innovative outcomes.

Teams and leaders who use this workbook are comfortable making decisions when not all the data is available. They are not looking for doctoral theories, but they do want confidence in knowing potential tools are the products of intellectual rigor. They strive to foster environments where intentions and processes are transparent. They are wholly committed to being people of integrity, deeply rooted in principles and values. They thrive in circumstances where they are called upon to solve problems using sound judgement, intent, vision, and conviction. They are committed to shaping the learning of others, especially those who are in most need of a chance to learn. They are imaginative and resourceful, and relish diversity and inclusion. They are instinctively compassionate toward those with whom they differ. These individuals and teams were whom I had in mind when I first undertook this journey.

I invite teams who are ready to change the world, starting with themselves and their relationships, to join me in gaining new perspectives in a critical effort to make a difference in troubled times. Research has proven that the use of teams results in increased productivity, a more responsible use of resources, and an overall better-quality service, product, or result (Northouse, 2012).

Effective team performance is based on each team member's mental model. The mental model is the team member's thought process of charting out all the possible risks and rewards they could encounter. They then move to develop the necessary contingencies to deal with anticipated conditions within the context of environmental and organizational constraints. In other words, effective teams are not lucky; on the contrary, they expect problems and have already mentally worked through possible solutions.

In order to nurture this mental model of thinking, teams must receive or seek training and supporting tool sets for the purposes of becoming comfortable with the inevitable unanticipated occurrences that are commonplace within organizations. Every team member must become comfortable with ever-changing demand signals, operations, contexts, and organizational structures. Leaders must help teams to focus on the overall result and not just "the process." This workbook was created for this specific purpose: to bring teams together and offer tools that support them at all levels – I Win (Individual); I make sure You Win (Relationships); We all Win (Organization, Community, Society).

Enjoy!

INTRODUCTION

The goal of increasing performance is an urgent and trending topic across many organizations and industries. Leaders are not only looking at information technologies, organizational structuring, and company policies for solutions, they understand that these enablers of performance are highly correlated with the level of commitment, focus, beliefs, and behaviors of individuals. People utilize, implement, maintain, and manage enablers to deliver value and desired outcomes. Leaders are more fully realizing, with great awe and angst, that their employees hold the key to organizational success. Establishing a highly functioning human system will be simultaneously their greatest challenge and utmost privilege.

How does one make the most of this opportunity? Many experts see the achievement of increased performance and impacts as largely a matter of leadership. There are literally hundreds of thousands of books, articles, teachings, and methodologies geared towards implementing effective leadership. However, there is far less content focused on leading teams for sustained peak performance, especially when considering the significant effort required to keep teams fully engaged. Leading for peak performance involves an in-depth understanding of the excruciatingly complex interconnectedness and the high degree of synchronized action that must occur for an enterprise to achieve continuous, reliable, repeatable high performance to attain its goals and outcomes.

For an organization to operate at these levels, a "we are all one" culture must emerge. This culture supports a "team of teams" essence. This culture chooses to possess a persistence towards partnership. This cultural construct adopts as its core value, "We are exponentially greater than the sum of our parts."

The *Winning Teams Workbook* was written to guide leaders, teams, and ultimately the organization towards this end. The Winning Teams Philosophy is based on the idea that "I Win. I make sure You Win. That way, We All Win." The *Winning Teams Workbook* is lightweight, straightforward, and it will supply leaders and their teams with exercises, activities, and assessments for increasing engagement, thoughtful reflection, and clarifying needs and next steps. Important findings of data and recent studies have been compiled, synthesized, and summarized to take leaders, their teams, and ultimately their organizations to the highest levels of performance and achievement.

In an "I win. I make sure YOU win. WE win!" world, people are not just responsible for their own personal success. With "I make sure YOU win," individuals are responsible for the success of their colleagues, teammates, and partners – those aligned under the same mission. Sometimes, we can perceive the actions of partners as oppositional, based on voiced perspectives or actions. Roles, responsibilities, and organizational structuring also have a way of placing team-mates at cross-purposes. Once individuals see themselves, their work, and their successes as connected, they work together in a more cooperative and collaborative manner. They take the time to understand the needs of their coun-terparts; they factor those needs into their definition of a win, resulting in a more holistic, all-encompassing posi-tive impact that results in the entire organization, winning. Hence, "We all win!"

I was introduced to this philosophy a few years ago while in casual conversation with Gilda, my mentor coach at the time. She and I worked together on an Organizational Culture Change project with heavy emphasis on Busi-ness and Performance Coaching. Three coaches, including myself, were being onboarded for the new project being rolled out. We were only a few days in when Gilda brought us together and emphasized the importance of the work we were embarking upon. At some point in the discussion, she shared, "I govern myself based on three wins – I win (I'm going to win). I make sure you win. That way, the whole organization wins."

In three simple sentences, she verbalized in the sim-plest and most elegant way how she engaged with oth-ers: from a space of confidence (I Win), care (I Make Sure You Win), and consistency (We All Win). Her assertion really resonated with me. Its utility in outlining a clear and transparent approach to figuring out how "we win" was profound and deeply compelling.

This workbook is the book I wish I had stumbled on so many years ago, when I first discovered my deep and enduring desire to lead, serve, and support people by modeling behaviors for the successful achievement of goals. This book contains many of my personal observations and perspectives, shaped by a career as a military leader and several years—post military—of working with organizations as a coach.

I have survived and thrived as a team leader, facilitator, executive, mentor, instructor, coach, and consultant in many different environments and organizations. I've led teams tasked with implementing cross-functional processes, contingency planning, and crisis response. I have served on several military staff teams, informing the decisions of senior officials as they weighed options, obstacles, and opportunities, and supervised several integral teams working in areas ranging from executive development to talent management.

These experiences are not outlined to say that each engagement was flawlessly executed; I continue to make many new mistakes that result in new learnings and understandings every day. There are no silver bullets. Each situation is unique and must be considered and responded to in its proper context. The exercises and activities I've laid out in this workbook have been extremely valuable in helping clients to stop, regroup, reflect, revisit, and quickly arrive at the next steps needed to move forward and continue their progress. This repeated cycle has reaped consistently high results for my teams, partners, customers, and the organizations with whom I have had the distinct privilege to work.

Exercise: What Would We Like to Have at the End of Our Engagement?

It is important for teams to hold themselves accountable to results.

Directions: Use this worksheet with your team to clarify your value proposition and build solid foundations for successful partnering. As a group, discuss the three questions below. Teams should revisit this page routinely and reflect on their collective results and learnings.

1. From a team perspective, which of the values listed below are essential to developing (or sustaining) a Winning Team? Check and then rank characteristics in order of highest to lowest.

	Check	Rank	
a)	_____	_____	Trust
b)	_____	_____	Communications
c)	_____	_____	Empathy
d)	_____	_____	Data-Driven Focus
e)	_____	_____	Transparency
f)	_____	_____	Partnering
g)	_____	_____	Mutual Respect
h)	_____	_____	Innovation
i)	_____	_____	Other _____

2. It can be difficult to tackle and overcome problems in a group, especially when tensions are high. Yet, circumstances are greatly improved when teams have a clear, concrete idea of their goal. Before embarking on any journey together, have team members take ten minutes to answer the following questions:

   a. What important positive outcomes will arise from our work?

   b. How would a Winning Team, operating at its highest potential, look?

   c. What new opportunities will we take advantage of together?

3. Describe an ideal scenario about your team interactions.

PART I

I WIN!!!!

CHAPTER 1

PERSONAL DEVELOPMENT

Experts advise leaders to make a conscious effort towards personal wholeness, noting that to transform and be transformational as a leader, it takes deep inner work over a long period. It cannot be achieved over the short-term and requires long-term dedication and commitment towards the mastery of acting ethically. Hultman (2002) counsels leaders that this level of intensive self-work is well worth the effort as they raise their professional level of performance and savor life more fully.

Leaders must know who they are in all circumstances. They must be in tune with their purpose for being. One does not need to know all the details in what the future holds if they are confident in the knowledge of who they are and how their values factor into whatever unpredictable future develops. Johnson and Geal (2015) recommend that leaders help guide their teams through trying and challenging times into places where they are creating futures, by leveraging their capacities in mindfulness, communication, and active listening. These were noted skills, which entailed personal and interpersonal components. These components involved interacting with teammates in a manner that was both assertive, yet non-prescriptive.

Leaders can cultivate these types of helping relationships by increasing their own self-awareness. The authors (2015) observe that as influencers, leaders must adapt to the culture of varying organizations and personalities. The leader's self-concept informs how followers see themselves in relation to others. Thus, driving their communication behaviors and improving the quality of their relationships has significant impacts on how a leader's value is perceived. Self-concept must be well developed for a leader to give their very best to the team. Leaders must constantly strive towards evolving, and finding better, more effective means of leading people. They must excel at developing cutting edge, quality products and services, fostering strong client and partner relationships, and effectively implementing strategy. This requires not only establishing but sustaining a learning environment that is inclusive and bridges differences automatically.

Latham (2014) poses the question: "Is it possible that the quest of the past 50-plus years to find a universal definition of effective leadership has been misguided and unattainable?" The point the author makes is that after several decades of study and research, there have been few convergences of theories that would typically be expected in other areas of leadership study with the voracity and emotion that the topic of leadership tends to arouse in researchers. Also, human beings—with their vast differences of experience, backgrounds, beliefs, and motives—are as a result immune to the "constraints of context" that many leadership studies use to frame their findings. Humanity's greatest gift is its ability to reason; it allows them to think up all types of reasons to justify doing exactly what they want to do. If they are not limited by current realities, they can easily envision a compelling future and set about on a plan to achieve whatever it is they feel most strongly about.

All things being similar and equal will still result in a surprisingly broad and vast range of results. As noted by C.S. Lewis (1980), "Man is at every moment subject to several sets of law but there is only one of these he is free to obey." In observing people's consistent compliance with laws of biology, laws of gravity, etc., we see that, curiously, a person can, at will, disobey human nature whenever they choose.

What then is a better approach to understanding leadership, since it involves predicting the unpredictable habits and tendencies of human beings? Latham (2014) recommends creating an agreement of knowledge, where seemingly unconnected and uncoordinated observations and findings combine and converge to form strong conclusions, supported commonalities within the studies, and methods and conclusions. The author also recommended creating a common comprehensive list of grading criteria for evidence of the effectiveness or ineffectiveness of leadership.

Latham (2014) observes that leadership studies are better served through the development of a framework by which various key factors of leadership—the leader, their behaviors, and their style—support a case for systems-based thinking, while maintaining the confidence, trust, and satisfaction of multiple, key supporters. Latham (2014) notes how this plays a key role in context because many leaders can make temporary improvements to a challenging situation, but if it is at the cost of sacrifices to other stakeholders, the effectiveness of the leader is only temporary and not a legitimate success.

Introducing Personal Development

Tools and Exercises

The tools and exercises in this section will help leaders increase their self-awareness related to their strengths and preferences. They will not only learn new skills and knowledge, but also learn about themselves, about others, and about the world and humanity.

These exercises may be used amongst team members to learn about others, discovering different viewpoints, values, and beliefs. They can aid in a discussion of getting to know others better. Additionally, these instruments will help participants identify gaps and opportunities for growth where their personal development is concerned.

Check List: Identifying Personal Qualities

This checklist has been developed to evaluate personal qualities, which might be significant to a team. The questions that follow the personal qualities are just meant to prompt reflection. Check the qualities that you feel apply to you.

☐ **Friendly:** Do you work well with others? Have you served on committees at school? At work? In the community?

☐ **Hard worker:** Do you work hard at your job or at school? Do you always put your best foot forward?

☐ **Cooperative:** Do you always do your part in a team assignment? Do you often volunteer to help?

☐ **Decisive:** Are you able to make clear-cut decisions under pressure?

☐ **Trustworthy:** Are you able to keep a secret? Do you guard confidential material carefully? Do you respect other people's right to privacy?

☐ **Efficient:** Do you plan your time well? Do you consciously try to improve your work habits?

☐ **Enthusiastic:** Are you interested in your work? Or studies? Have you ever done extra work because of your interest?

☐ **Honest:** Do you tell the truth? Do you share the praise with others? Do you accept responsibility?

☐ **Self-starter:** Do you take the initiative? Do you see what needs to be done and do it without being told?

Check List: Identifying Personal Qualities (Cont'd)

☐ **Open-minded:** Are you able to accept other ideas? Do you adapt well?

☐ **Orderly:** Do you keep things where they belong? Do you have a knack for arranging things in a logical way?

☐ **Patient:** Can you keep your temper? Are you able to train other workers calmly even when you must explain some procedures over and over again?

☐ **Punctual:** Do you consistently arrive on time?

☐ **Sympathetic:** Do you try to understand the problems of others? Do people confide in you often? Do you help them?

☐ **Strong:** Can you lift things that are heavy?

☐ **Team player:** Do you work well with others? Can you work as part of a team?

Exercise: Acknowledging and Supporting Yourself

Acknowledging yourself and your positive attributes is a great way to be positive at work.

Write down up to five strengths, for example: friendly, happy, generous – I enjoy giving (time, money, support) to causes I am passionate about.

1. _____

2. _____

3. _____

4. _____

5. _____

Write down up to five great achievements in your life so far, like recovering from a serious illness, learning to use a computer, raising your children, going back to school, etc.

1. _____

2. _____

3. _____

4. _____

5. _____

Exercise: Acknowledging and Supporting Yourself (Cont'd)

Write down five things you can do to help someone else, like taking care of their children for an evening, visiting someone in the hospital, just reaching out with a friendly call, etc.

1. _____

2. _____

3. _____

4. _____

5. _____

Write down five things you can do to make yourself feel better, like calling a friend, going for a walk, taking a bath, etc.

1. _____

2. _____

3. _____

4. _____

5. _____

Chapter 2

VALUES AND ETHICS

Much is required of leaders, and much is at stake. Recently, heightened scrutiny has befallen those in positions of leadership in the wake of corporate and political scandals, and a seemingly unending wave of leaders failing in every organizational context imaginable. The result is that today, leadership has become synonymous with abuse and manipulation of the vulnerable and powerless, narcissistic, selfish acts and unwarranted, undeserved advantage and preference. Being a leader is no longer noble in the eyes of many. But it can be.

Many of today's leaders suffer from a crisis of conscience. Ayers (2006) observes that the moral and ethical void present in many leaders results in a lack of vision, confidence, and purpose. The author goes on to note that many spiritual leaders—pastors, ministers, evangelists— note declining effectiveness, which they tend to blame on inadequate theological training and insufficient overall preparation to lead congregations or any spiritual organization, be it youth group, Bible study, or a ministry. This crisis of conscience is actually a crisis of ethics!

More and more, what people do and carry out have no alignment with their internal values. Leaders are willingly conducting and overlooking unethical or borderline practices to gain more power, money or esteem, oblivious to the trade-offs of lack of control, internal conflict, guilt, shame, decreased credibility, lost trust, and diminished respect among followers. However, this can be turned around by leaders realizing their impact on their organizations' ethical climate, getting clear about what their ethics are, and holding steadfast to those convictions. To be successful, leaders must maintain a fundamental framework by which to process emergent, wildly complex ethical decisions.

Many of the patterns and perspectives we apply throughout our lives were acquired in early childhood because at that time, a person is most susceptible to learning and assimilating. Hofstede et al (2010) refer to this phenomenon as the individual's unique programming. The sources of each individual's mental programming lie within the social environments in which they were brought up, and the compositions of their life's experiences. The programming begins in the family; it continues within their neighborhood, their school, in religious forums and other organized social groups, at work, and extends throughout their community (Hofstede et al, 2010).

In recognition of the individual programming most leaders show up with as they assume their role, Yoos II and Barker (2008) recommend the use of "covenons," a term which combines the nouns "covenant" and "values," to define the use of commitments (promises) made by leaders to place values that are important to the organization into context. According to the authors, covenons are not just static, unchangeable artifacts that get stuck on the wall. Covenons are the true expression of the organization's and employees' character, a character that is always a work in progress. It is continually improving, and strengthened or weakened, and reinforced with each action. Covenons express the commitment (covenant) of each member of the organization to be better (thus, aligning with shared values) in every transaction, interaction, and activity of work.

Virtue, character, and responsibility all play competing roles in influencing the ethical decisions that leaders make. Each of these are extremely important because they are personal and based on who the individual is, how they process information, their personal biases and experiences, and what they identify as, based on external perceptions, titles, and positions held.

Virtue ethics call on individuals to develop and establish their own personal code of ethics and not rely on antiquated and irrelevant principles to which they offer only half-hearted compliance (Levy, 2004). When someone is clear about their values, it shows up in the work they do. Their work aligns to a greater purpose, and a whole new framing of their work unfolds. Hughes and Beatty (2005) relay a story of two stonemasons working, both laying down mortar and putting down bricks. When asked what they were doing, one replies, "I'm laying bricks," and the other replies, "I'm building a cathedral."

The leader holds an integral role in framing projects in terms that will elicit either a head or heart response. The extent to which people dedicate themselves to their work depends on whether the leader lays out clear and compelling aspirations, and this starts with a clear moral compass of their own. Hultman (2002) shares that a person's values perform the three key actions of:

1. Preventing exposure to perceived threats
2. Orienting the individual to society, and
3. Spurring growth

Shared values foster feelings of personal achievement, encourage ethical behavior, foster teamwork, and promote high levels of loyalty (Kouzes and Posner, 2012). By being clear and transparent about who they are and what they value, leaders can alleviate any confusion or sense of ambivalence about what is considered standard ethical behavior.

Pruzan (2008) notes that the importance of leaders' inner perspective is foundational for actions and decisions made in the outer business world. The author goes on to predict that the next big crisis in business is not going to be conflicts that take place between people, but instead conflicts that take place within people.

Introducing Values and Ethics Tools and Exercises

 The tools and exercises in this section will help leaders take inventory of their values and ethics. The threat of internal conflict being the next big leadership crisis is real. With the constant influx of new information and demands on leaders, finding one's place to take a stand can feel like standing on sand while waves continuously strip away all that is underfoot. This book and the exercises within give leaders a more solid foundation during these constantly changing times.

These exercises can also help teams identify shared values and better understand the team's ethics. Lastly, these instruments assist in the development of team and individual covenants to establish clear boundaries to remain in personal alignment.

Exercise: Exploring Personal Values and Beliefs

Write five statements about what is most important for you as a team member. If being on time is very important to you, you might write a statement like this:

I will be on time for team meetings each day because being on time shows respect to my co-workers, teammates, key stake-holders, and boss.

If working hard is very important to you, you might write a statement like this:

Working hard shows my team and leadership that I have initiative and am interested in opportunities for taking on greater responsibility.

Your Turn!

1. _____

   _____

2. _____

   _____

3. _____

   _____

4. _____

   _____

5. _____

   _____

Exercise: Exploring Personal Values and Beliefs (Cont'd)

Instructions: Considering that individuals are a compilation of their values and behaviors, which factor into their decisions and behaviors, answer these:

1. What is the one value for which you wish to be remembered in your family, your community, your work, and in your life?

_____

_____

2. List actions you have taken that demonstrate this value, or outcomes you have achieved as a result of holding this value?

_____

_____

3. To what extent are you aware of your emotions? To what extent do you understand rationally why you react the way you do?

_____

_____

4. How well do you understand how your values, principles, and goals develop?

_____

_____

Exercise: Exploring Personal Values and Beliefs (Cont'd)

5. How effective are you in recognizing when your fundamental belief systems are challenged? How methodical are you in reconciling these challenges?

_____

_____

6. How effectively do you state your point of view?

_____

_____

Chapter 3

COACHING

The International Coach Federation, the premiere credentialing body for coaches across the globe, defines coaching as "partnering with clients in a thought-provoking and creative process that inspires them to maximize their personal and professional potential." Michael Simpson (2014), author of *Unlocking Potential: 7 Coaching Skills That Transform Individuals, Teams and Organizations*, observes that coaching is "unleashing or unlocking the potential of another human being."

These definitions recognize the infinite potential of mastering and bringing to bare an individual's own unique, innate strengths and talents. As an "I Win" activity, leaders can invest in and participate in coaching services when available. Coaching has long been proven to increase performance, raise self-awareness, and increase self-confidence, which leads to self-fulfillment and, in due course, self-actualization (Whitmore, 2013).

There are four principal varieties of coaching which include:

- Coaching (general)
- Business Coaching
- Leadership (Executive) Coaching, and
- Personal Coaching

This segment deals primarily with the impact of Leadership Coaching, which differs from the other coaching approaches because it helps its clients (leaders within their organizations) know themselves better, and feel more comfortable with who they are and how they show up as leaders on teams and within the organization.

Kets de Vries (2008) asserts that leadership coaching is an intervention that can be implemented strategically with both individuals and teams throughout the entire organization. Its purpose is to bring people together towards mutually agreed upon goals and objectives. Leadership coaching accelerates organizational growth through its provision for focus and awareness. Unlike other personal development catalysts, like mentoring and leadership training, coaching is an enabler to growth and not necessarily a tool to be implemented for growth.

The reason coaching is an enabler and not implemented is because of the belief system that coaches embrace – coaching assumes that all the "right" answers and actions rest within the person being coached; coaching does not strive to put the right answers into the person being coached. It does not endeavor to modify or correct the answers once the client has arrived at what the right decision is for them. It accepts and embraces whatever decision clearly aligns with the client's values, beliefs, priorities, and goals (Gatling and Harrah, 2014).

Crabb (2011) states that coaching and positive psychology can offer major support as means of supporting a leader's personal development, as well as increasing the leader's engagement with their followers. However, it is important to understand the distinctions between the two approaches:

- Coaching involves a developmental conversation
- Positive psychology denotes the framework that has been proven highly effective in framing questions in ways that facilitate a productive actionable solution

Combined, leaders can use both methods to help people excel, succeed, and grow as members of the organization. From there, leaders can also focus on enhancing team member skills, esprit de corps, work happiness, and job satisfaction. They avoid wasting time and resources trying to "plug" gaps in order to meet highly subjective performance standards. The essence of coaching promotes what makes people excel, succeed, and grow as organization members.

Recent research trends indicate that CEOs who harden themselves, convinced they do well to keep their own counsel and trust their own instincts, soon realize their need for unbiased advice, new perspectives and thinking, and coaching. For this, they typically turn to lawyers, investment bankers and, of course, their management consultant. Management consultants equipped with coaching training are in an even better position to understand active listening techniques, direct communications, the importance of challenging assumptions, and the benefits of powerful questioning (Coach U, 2005).

Common Coaching Topics

In a study (Coach U, 2005), assessing more than 1,000 booked coaching appointments, the following topics ranked highest:

- **Self-leadership** - identifying and managing priorities, handling change, finding motivation, overcoming procrastination, managing time, forming or reducing habits, managing your energy
- **Life skills** - setting goals, decision making, problem solving, managing stress, getting organized, scheduling, project planning, drawing boundaries, acquiring support
- **Life perspectives** - seeking happiness, hearing your calling, defining success, overcoming adversity, preparing for transition, understanding and then utilizing your strengths

Limits to Coaching

Coaching is about seeing the best in you and working to move you closer to your goals. Coaching works for nearly anyone, whether you just want to refine goals and strategies you already have, or work on significant change by establishing it from the ground up. Coaching works for anyone who is committed to a better path forward, regardless of age, academic level, and life experience. Coaching can cover nearly any topic that affects your current perspectives and plans, as well as how you desire to move forward in your family, field of study, or workplace. However, coaching is not counseling as we are not licensed, and we do not diagnose or prescribe treatment; it is also not academic advising as we do not assist with policies and procedures, registration, or degree planning. While the conversations are confidential, we cannot keep in confidence intent to self-harm, harm to others, or abuse. Still, coaching can be quite powerful and has few limitations.

Introducing Coaching Tools and Exercises

The tools and exercises in this section introduce some quickly applicable coaching frameworks that can be used to start a highly productive and insightful conversation. To be fully effective, coaching conversations must be utilized in concert with such skills as active listening, presence, and positive intent. Consider giving these areas a bit of research before engaging beyond initial coach-oriented discussions with team members. It is also highly recommended that you seek out a professional coach to provide mentorship or even facilitate team-wide discussions.

These exercises can also help teams identify shared and divergent understandings of a shared situation and foster productive dialogue for solutions-focused collaborations in situations where finger-pointing and blame-seeking often prevail.

Quick Reference: Introducing GROW Model of Coaching

With slight variation, the specific questions in each of the four areas of the Goals, Realities, Options, and Way Ahead (GROW) model can be enormously helpful in using the process with teams.

Goal
- What do you want from our time?
- What is the most important outcome from today's discussion?
- How will we know we were successful in our coaching conversation?

Way Ahead
- What next steps are you ready to commit to?
- What will you be happy to report during our next meeting?
- What support do you need?
- When will you do this?

Reality
- What have you tried so far?
- What is the reality of this situation, as you see it?
- What aspects of this situation can you realistically influence or control?

Options
- Who and what can you leverage to support outcomes that are favorable?
- Being your boldest and most resourceful self, what could you do?
- If you could not fail, how would you proceed?

Figure 2 GROW Model with sample questions.

Quick Reference: GROW Questions*

Goal

What topic do we want to discuss?

What do we want from this discussion? (What's our Specific, Measurable, Action-based, Relevant/realistic, Time-based (S.M.A.R.T.) Goal?)

What are the consequences if we do not reach this goal?

Reality

Briefly, what's been happening?

What have we tried so far? What were the results?

What's our sense of the obstacles in front of us?

Considering others (if others are involved)? Is this goal still realistic?

Options

Describe fantasyland: if we could do anything, what might we do?

If others are involved, what would they need to see or hear to get their attention? If we were watching this conversation, what would we recommend?

Do any of these ideas interest us enough to explore further? If we were to do this, how might we go about it?

Way Forward

Does this option interest us enough to act?

How will we go about it?

What might get in the way? How might we overcome that?

Quick Reference: GROW Questions* (Cont'd)

What and when is the next step?

* Adapted from, Fine, Alan; Merrill, Rebecca R. (2012) *You Already Know How to Be Great: A Simple Way to Remove Interference and Unlock Your Greatest Potential* (p. 149). Penguin Publishing Group.

CHAPTER 4

LEADERSHIP COMMUNICATION

Hackman and Johnson (2009) assert that it is extremely important for a speaker to integrate emotion and cognition into their communication with audiences. Especially in urgent or emotionally charged situations, speakers are advised to skillfully blend their feelings and thinking to authentically connect with groups of personnel, partners, or stakeholders. It is vital to successful communication to have the ability to discern and identify what is the most important message and information to convey, evaluating what concerns or aspirations must be addressed and then expressing next steps in a transparent, practical, and intentional way.

A leader must communicate clearly, consistently, and continuously. In order to be an effective leader, one must become an effective communicator. Three activities that enable him or her to do this include:

1. Developing the appropriate leadership message
2. Delivering a message that is consistent, and
3. Sustaining the message

It is impossible to over-practice or over-prepare when delivering a key message. Leaders' preparations give them clarity, intention, and boldness so that they can confidently go forth and present their desires to any audience and experience a positive response (Baldoni, 2014).

Seldom are there circumstances when leaders' interventions are not polarizing. Sometimes situations call for a high stakes conversation. High stakes conversations are difficult but essential conversations that all leaders must master. They are most effective when opposing positions exist, emotions are intensified, and of course, there are great risks or rewards. Often, those affected believe there are only two options: avoid the conversation or lose the relationship by directly addressing uncomfortable truths. But these conversations are of great importance and with the right approach, can result in stronger relationships and resolved issues (Patterson et al, 2012).

Empathy is a core leadership communication behavior. *Webster's New World Dictionary* defines empathy as, "the projection of one's own personality into the personality of another in order to understand the person better; the ability to share in another's emotions, thoughts or feelings."

Hose (2012) tells leaders that to be effective they must excel in their ability to communicate ideas to the "three Cs": the Consumer, the Customer, and the Chief Executives. In order to do this, empathy is required. Empathy is essential for creating an environment where people will be willing to change. By using empathy—one of the key foundations of Emotional Intelligence (EQ)–leaders can identify with all three "C" perspectives and find the commonalities that will energize these three diverse audiences to action.

Goleman (2013) goes so far as to offer that effectively communicating as a leader is less about fully understanding all the details and circumstances, or even mastering skill sets, than it is about developing a genuine interest in and talent for fostering positive feelings in people whose cooperation and support is needed for success. In Johnson and Hackman's *Leadership: A Communication's Perspective* (2018), the authors share that in order to be an effective leader, one must become an effective communicator. Three actions help to ensure success in this objective:

- Developing the appropriate leadership message
- Delivering a message that is consistent
- Sustaining the message

Another secret that is a good fit for this cycle is adding illustration to the message. If anything can engage the fullest part of the brains and senses (Denning, 2007) it is definitely props and visuals that push the message even further into the audience's psyche and bring the leader's message home more clearly, with even more of a lasting effect. Denning (2007) notes how in Shakespeare's *Julius Caesar* when Marc Anthony waved the bloody tunic of a slain Caesar it immediately roused interest and sympathy amongst the masses. These instrumental props and symbolic illustrations can be powerful if the leader uses objects that are immediately recognizable by their audience and not something irrelevant, ambiguous, or potentially overly offensive or polarizing: they will serve to disperse rather than unite.

Advertisers and marketers tend to agree that repetition is an effective tool for narrative and a secret that should be added to Baldoni's (2014) list. Denning (2007) notes that it is one thing to get people excited about a worthwhile idea, but another to keep the energy up. Trust in the leader is paramount in keeping people resolute when challenges arise. Leaders must be very aware and ready to remedy the challenges of loss of momentum, loss of focus, and risks for outsiders who view the activities of changes as chaos.

Denning (2007) also cautions leaders who are charged with reinforcing and reiterating their stories that they must ensure any main characters are consistently portrayed to ensure perceptions of the character's actions are reliable and predictable across situations. The story should also be minimalist in nature and told without a great deal of context and detail. Too many details may paint contradictory accounts and an unstable picture of how a particular event or future may look depending on who's retelling the story, or the audience hearing the story.

For example, if a leader is preparing a team for an upcoming change, they must be clear on why the change must occur (client demands, regulatory requirements, etc.). They must be clear about the realities (new opportunities, risks avoided, need for new positions, skill sets, processes, tools, etc.). They must clearly and consistently maintain the narrative of why change is necessary, what will be required, and what success will look like (we will know we are on track when we see successful compliance, acquired skill sets, and positive customer response).

The leader must remain firmly engaged with the people and his or her message to ensure that trust in the leader is maintained, and that people will continue to support their commitments. Examples of this include using statements which reveal humanity and vulnerability, refraining from technical jargon and speaking plainly and on message, and dressing the part, which demonstrates communion and connection with the audience (Hackman and Johnson, 2009).

Introducing Leadership Communication Tools and Exercises

Leaders can use this section's tools and exercises to help them assess their current standing related to their communications efforts. Tools will also help leaders and teams to think through their communications and ensure they hit the right audience, strike the right tone, and elicit the desired action.

These exercises can also help a team identify often overlooked opportunities for leaders to communicate more effectively with diverse audiences and constituencies, thus inviting better feedback and discussions which support heightened innovation and team morale.

Self-Assessment: Test Your Communication Skills

Fill in the chart below and tally up your communication score at the end.

	Often	Sometimes	Never
1. I can detect the mood of others by looking at them when we talk.			
2. I can tell when someone doesn't understand what I am saying.			
3. I can discuss issues without getting upset.			
4. I find it easy to understand someone else's point of view.			
5. When talking to people, I pay attention to their body language.			
6. When I am angry, I admit it.			
7. I express my ideas clearly.			
8. I change the way I talk depending on who I'm speaking to.			
9. I express my opinions, even if others do not agree.			
10. I can talk about my feelings.			
11. When I know what someone will say, I finish their sentence.			
12. I find it hard to express my feelings to others.			
13. I have difficulty putting my thoughts into words.			

Self-Assessment: Test Your Communication Skills (Cont'd)

14. People tend to misinterpret what I say.			
15. I fidget while listening to someone talk.			
16. People don't understand what I am talking about.			
17. If I find a conversation boring, I'll let my mind drift away.			
18. I will stop a speaker in mid-sentence if I disagree with a statement he or she made.			
19. People complain that I don't appear to be listening when they speak to me.			
20. I tend to do most of the talking in conversations.			
21. I repeat myself often because people don't understand what I am saying the first time.			
22. I find it difficult to understand someone when they have a different point of view from mine.			
23. If I have something relevant to add, I'll interrupt someone to make certain my views are heard.			
24. When other people become emotional around me, I'm not sure how to react.			

Self-Assessment: Test Your Communication Skills (Cont'd)

Calculate your score!

Questions 1 - 10

3 points for Often _____

2 points for Sometimes _____

0 points for Never _____

Total A _____

Questions 11- 25

0 points for Often _____

2 points for Sometimes _____

3 points for Never _____

Total B _____

Total A _____ *plus Total B* _____ = _____

Results

50-75: You are an excellent communicator!

25-50: You have fairly good communication skills, but still need some help.

0-25: You need some help with your communication skills.

Sample: Leader Communications Plan

Think through or write out a plan for communications.

1. Determine the audience to receive the message.
    a. Who are the key players?
    b. What is their interest and influence?
    c. Who is the primary and secondary audience?
2. Focus in on what you want to achieve.
    a. What is your goal?
    b. What objectives will be met through communications?
    c. What outcomes will communications achieve?
3. Prepare clear, direct messages.
    a. What is your intent for engaging the audience?
    b. What do you want the audience to do?
    c. What is important for the audience to learn?
4. Leverage diverse approaches.
    a. What verbal communications will you use?
    b. What nonverbal communications will you use?
    c. What visual communications will you use?
5. Assess effectiveness.
    a. How will you measure communications efficiency?
    b. How will you measure communications effectiveness?
    c. What feedback mechanism will you leverage (surveys, questionnaires, dashboard, etc.)?

Tool: Guidelines for Metrics, Data Analysis, and Timing Communications

Use these practices, tips, and recommendations to determine the quality and impacts of your communications.

When it comes to communications, timing is crucial. Consider the time suggestions below based on research on communications timing.

1. **Recommendation**: Determine what metrics to track. **How to do it**: Look at options and decide, and ask yourself the following:
   a. What constitutes a successful communication (# of emails opened, positive interactions, happier employees, etc.)?
   b. What tools/resources can you leverage to collect data?
   c. What's the working hypothesis you will validate/ nullify?
2. **Recommendation**: Consider General Timing... **How to do it**: See the statistics on the next page based on research from the leaders in communications management platforms (MailChimp, Campaign Monitor, Constant Contact, and Active Campaign):

Tool: Guidelines for Metrics, Data Analysis, and Timing Communications (Con't)

Figure 2.   According to the Email research from the platforms mentioned, prioritize send days in this order:

1st Place: Tuesday	2nd Place: Thursday	3rd Place: Wednesday
Hands down, the best day to send emails according to most studies.	If you send e-mails twice a week, choose Thursday as the second day.	While no single study showed that Wednesday was the most popular, it came in second place several times.

Figure 3. Platform experts recommend arranging send times based on the below data:

1st Place: 10 a.m.

While late-morning send times were the most popular in general, several concluded that the best time to send emails is at 10 a.m. Another notable time is 11 a.m.

2nd Place: 8 p.m.- midnight

I bet you didn't expect that one. It looks like emails generally receive more opens and clicks later in the evening. As Campaign Monitor notes, this is likely due to people checking their email before going to bed.

3rd Place: 2 p.m.

It looks like you might be successful by sending your emails later in the day as people are checking out of work mode or looking for distractions.

4th Place: 6 a.m.

I guess this makes sense since 50% of you begin your day by emailing in bed. Before you even stand up, you're opening emails.

Tool: Guidelines for Metrics, Data Analysis, and Timing Communications (cont'd)

3. **Recommendation**: Look at your data.

   How to do it: Depending on software, you may be able to see analytics related to timing. Otherwise, study the flow of key communications manually. Keep notes and experiment with your findings. Even with the recommendations and tips provided, there is no substitute for testing these findings with your own audience.

PROFILE OF AN "I WIN"

You're operating from your inner "I Win" when you are confidently taking on the world. New challenges bring you energy, which enables you to invest incredible time and talent while avoiding the experience of burnout. This is mainly because attaining goals and setting new ones brings a sense of satisfaction.

Throughout each endeavor and new position, it is the "I Win" in us that recognizes when to go it alone and when to request and receive support, heeding to wise counsel. The "I Win" within allows us to transition from a novice leader into a highly capable, impactful, and evolved leader.

Velsor et al (2010) share that leader development includes experiences, and notes that not all leader experiences are created equal. As years go on in one position, new experiences plateau and then become far less frequent than when a leader initially assumed a position. A leader, having worked in several different leadership roles may be found to have a broader, more developed leader experience than someone who has stayed in the same role over several years.

"Throw me to the wolves and I will come back leading the pack."

~Unknown (Sentiments of an "I Win")

An "I Win" individual is highly adaptable and intentionally evolves their own development by seeking opportunities in deepening their self-awareness, and their coaching and communication skills. In an "I Win" state of mind, those around you see the distinct approaches and decisions that lead to your success and how you adapt to each new position with grace, humility, wisdom, and integrity. In each position you're placed, you proclaim: "I Win!!"

PART II

I MAKE SURE
YOU WIN!!!!

Chapter 5

LEADERSHIP DEVELOPMENT

Johnson (2009) notes that leadership, when cultivated for the next generation of leaders, is an apostolic gift. This person is a fire starter who digs into the trenches, creates something from nothing, and then moves on to something else, leaving the people fully trained and able to carry on the work for themselves. The author believes that leaders who build new leaders plant the seeds of success in other people by showering them with information, resources, sharing networks, and best practices. These leaders let members "shadow" them to see and not just have explained how the work got done.

Velsor et al (2010) observes that effective organizational systems for leader development include the essential components of: Assessment, Challenge, and Support. These components create the ideal foundation for an effective leader development program. The assessment component of the leader development involves creating a baseline, an initial starting point. From there, challenge is introduced to grow and stretch the individual leaders being developed. Lastly, support is provided to ensure that those new skill sets obtained, and knowledge gained, are adopted as behaviors, and implemented fully into the working knowledge of the leader. Leader development that involves lots of practice and time for application and challenge assists participants in reflection and facilitates deeper examination of past experiences. These components provide a better development experience than traditional leader development, which had only provided new leaders with information.

This approach outlines the need for greater attention and care in the leadership development process. In an "I make sure you win" world, leaders do not take shortcuts when the time comes to train other leaders. They take on the task with love. Sanborn (2010) explains that the word "love" makes people uneasy and uncomfortable, yet, he argues, it can also be the word that makes you and your work irresistible! The author acknowledges that while there are no perfect jobs in this imperfect world, it is possible to love the work we perform. He uses the acronym "P-R-A-C-T-I-C-E-S" to remember the powerful upside of adding love to your work; it reflects the principles of **P**atience, **R**ecognition, **A**ppreciation, **C**ounsel, **T**ime, **I**nstruction, **C**ompassion, **E**ncouragement and **S**ervice.

By lovingly approaching leadership and leader development from a position of charity, the leader developer's focus is not on themselves and their agenda, but on how they can best develop tools to help others accomplish their goals and realize their highest potential. According to Guinness (2003), much of the greatness of the human spirit can be witnessed while observing our passionate pursuit of knowledge, truth, justice, beauty, perfection, and love, all things we can experience in our selected occupations.

Leader development support systems facilitate and promote initiatives by compelling those in or aspiring to leadership to focus on learning, growth, and change. Additionally, these systems provide untainted data for learning, cases and real-world examples that facilitated knowledge, understanding, and the application of wisdom. It can also spur shifts in perspectives to uncover new and innovative thinking. Velsor et al (2010) aver that leader development includes experiences (and note that not all leader experiences are created equal); as years go on in one position, new experiences plateau, and then become far less frequent than when a leader initially assumed a position. A leader, having worked in several different leadership roles may be found to have a broader, more developed leader experience than someone who stayed in the same role over several years.

Leadership development experts have identified the approach of "reverse mentoring" to break down the old paradigm belief that mentoring is only a relationship where someone with more experience can pass it down to someone with less experience in a field. The fact is that everyone has something to teach us. Reverse mentoring is especially impactful in cases when everyone acknowledges the experience and expertise the other needs to contribute to organizational performance. Reverse mentoring is not just choosing two people of different ages and then engaging them in dialogue. To be most productive, leaders should consider the following guidelines to get their programs set up for success (Bolser and Gosciej, 2015):

1. **Purposefully Pairing**. Partners should have the expertise and skills their counterparts need.

2. **Encourage Evolution**. Meet with participants to convey goals for bringing them together, emphasize how much you believe each person can learn from the other, and set expectations.

3. **Coach along the way**. Train each participant in mentoring or coaching as needed.

4. **Establish Definitive Goals**. Have each pair agree on what they want to accomplish and how/when to measure the results.

5. **Develop Consistency**. Have pairs meet on a regular schedule and communicate between meetings, by phone or online.

For leaders, there is always something urgent, pressuring, or requiring immediate attention. However, we must ensure that our next generations of leaders benefit from our experiences and lessons learned along the way. Leaders must be mindful of how our day-to-day decisions have long-term consequences. The futures of our organizations are the result of the things we choose and choose not to do every day. We must constantly assess our environment, identify what could cause an issue, and do everything possible to mitigate or remove those obstacles that threaten the future of our organizations and teams.

One final note on diversity: as leaders we should be cautioned not to just "clone" ourselves. Northouse (2012) warns against leaders' tendencies towards homosocial reproduction. People tend to have the best opinions and biases towards people most like them. He notes this often creates a disadvantage for minorities and women, and often extends to religious, ethnicity, and sexual orientation. Being a leader and possessing the vision are just first steps. Getting training is essential because we cannot assume everyone's positions and experiences have set them up to perform successfully as leaders. We must be mindful that much like we do in the military forces, successful organizations start introducing leadership concepts as soon as new trainees walk through the door.

Introducing Leader Development Tools and Exercises

As a leader, you'll face internal and external situations that challenge your resolve. When you are aware of your attitudes and personality, you'll be better prepared to approach the task at hand, delegate responsibilities, work with others, and communicate during high-pressure situations.

In this section, leaders will find tools and exercises that will help them evaluate their proficiency in effectively developing other leaders. These tools and exercises are perfect for spurring conversations around the partnering agreement and the mentor/mentee contract. Tools will also help leaders and emerging leaders to think through their communications and ensure they present the right way, to the right audience, striking the right tone and eliciting the desired response or actions.

Self-Assessment: Leader Developmnt Competency

"Leaders don't create followers; they create more leaders."

~ Tom Peters

Instructions: Fill in the chart below; tally up your leadership development competency score at the end.

	Confident	Competent	Learning
Create a climate of trust			
Facilitate relationships			
Enhance self-determination in others			
Develop competence and confidence			
Model the way			
Become a lifelong learner			
Present a professional demeanor			

Calculate your score!
3 points for Confident
2 points for Competent
0 points for Learning

Total = _ _ _ _

Results
16 – 21: You are an excellent developer of leaders!
10 – 15: You are a competent leader developer, with opportunity to grow.
0 – 10: You will want to enlist some help with leader development skills.

Sample: Mentor/ Mentee Contract (Leader Development Agreement)

Making the leadership development relationship official is helpful for making the expectation and purpose for the arrangement clear between all parties. Consider using this agreement, if you believe it will prove beneficial to clarify roles, responsibilities, and expectations.

Objectives:
Working together, we hope to achieve: _____

_____

_____

We will do this by (measures for success): _____

_____

_____

Confidentiality: Mentor (leader) will honor the confidentiality of everything discussed. In addition, it is agreed the following topics are beyond the scope:

_____

_____

Frequency: We will meet ____ times a Month (Quarter) on _____ (Either pick a recurring time or determine who reaches out to whom to coordinate meetings).

Plan for evaluating relationship effectiveness: Select 1 or 2 metrics and a time period for assessing how well objectives are being met (e.g., a bi-annual review of mentorship meeting minutes, goals, and outcomes):

_____

_____

_____

No-Fault Termination: Both parties are committed to open and honest communications. We will discuss and attempt to resolve any conflicts as they arise. If at any time, either party must terminate this relationship for any reason, we agree to abide by one another's decision.

Mentor Signature _____   Protégé Signature _____

Date _____   Date _____

CHAPTER 6

PARTNERING

Partnering is a critical competitive competency for any leader wanting to drive sustainable growth through innovation. In fact, it would not be an overstatement to state that the success of innovative leaders and teams hinges on the quality and longevity of their collaborative relationships.

Ecclesiastes 4:9-10 (Holy Bible, KJV) tells us, "Two are better than one because they have a good reward for their labor. For if they fall, the one will lift up his fellow: but woe to him that is alone when he falleth; for he hath not another to help him up."

Numerous research studies and professional literature suggest that in complex environments of novelty and disruption, variety in perspective, experience, and talent can result in more valuable information being offered and applied to the issue (Durst and Ziegert, 2012).

The importance of partnering is not new wisdom, and in today's highly interconnected and intricate world, we are far more connected than we often choose to realize. Particularly in the realm of business, partnerships are important and essential to success, especially in times when the market/customer environment is tough and formidable. It is good to know there is a partner to help with recovery and "getting back up" after a fall. Partnerships have the potential to increase leadership impacts exponentially and synergize the best of two entities, making the total greater than the sum of its parts.

Hunter et al (2012) tell us that specifically in areas where innovation is key, a "leadership duo" is a better fit than a lone leader. Their premise being that the creative (vision/ideation/conception) and management (execution/planning/organizing/executing) expertise seldom reside in one individual. Brilliant leaders are typically far more one than they are the other, so it is difficult to bridge that gap, in terms of concept, and even more challenging, from a workload perspective. It supports the adage of "two heads are better than one."

There are some exceptions. Hunter et al (2012) submit that in every partnering there is not a guarantee of success, but there are things partners can do to ensure a highly beneficial coupling. An important indicator for success in a "leadership dyad" is that, first and foremost, the project is at the center of the relationship. Further, all decisions and approaches must ultimately be accepted or rejected based on their benefit or risk to the project. Partnership should benefit projects by ensuring that more gets done than either party could achieve on their own. In partnerships, there are naturally places where each partner will want to pull back, digress, and proceed more cautiously than the situation might warrant. In those cases, it is important to push each other to build capacity, address concerns, and take whatever steps are necessary to achieve the highest possible targets and ensure maximum impact for the sake of customers and stakeholders.

In addition to the partnership having a project focus, trust must be established. Trust is an important factor in ensuring a long, successful partnership. Hackman and Johnson (2009) state that trust in leadership-dyads and partnerships is paramount in keeping people resolute when challenges arise. Leaders must be very aware and ready to remedy the challenges of loss of momentum, loss of focus, and risks for outsiders who view the activities of changes as chaos.

The leader must remain firmly engaged with people and with their own message to ensure that trust is maintained, and that people will continue to support their commitments. Examples of engagement include using statements which reveal humanity and vulnerability, refraining from technical jargon and speaking plainly while informing, and dressing the part to demonstrate communion and connection with the audience. Partners must carry themselves and handle their duties in ways that will garner and maintain trust (Hackman and Johnson, 2009).

Another criterion for a successful partnership is that it must be understood and accepted as a partnership of equals. Genuine mutual respect and appreciation for each other's skills, commitment, and contributions is required. In the partnership between Steve Jobs and Tim Cook, Steve Jobs was the expert out in front of customers and board members, sharing ideas and delivering the perfect pitch.

However, many argue that Steve would not have been nearly as successful if Tim Cook had not been the details and organizing expert: supporting, coordinating, and overseeing logistics, marketing, management, and administration (Hunter et al, 2012).

Above all, for any good partnership to endure and sustain success, communication is key. All members of the partnership must be able to clearly articulate vision, inviting the entire organization to support a worthwhile endeavor. Denning (2007) notes that when an activity is pursued for its own sake and not for some internal or external benefit such as money, prestige, power or even "winning," the inherent worth bestowed on the activity increases the likelihood that it will be enduring.

Introducing Partnering Tools and Exercises

This section familiarizes leaders with some quickly applicable partnering exercises and assessments that can be used to spark inspired and engaging collaborations. Joining efforts is no small endeavor. It takes a lot of work, dedication, vision, and humility to come together to be part of something greater.

Using these tools involves understanding the strengths and motives of those entering the partnership. Use these tools as talking points for a partnering conversation. Typically, partnerships are built on necessity and while this is typical, these necessary moments can be enhanced and made a more productive and even enjoyable experience.

Exercise: Qualities of Effective Team Partners

What are some qualities of an effective teaming partner? i.e., friendly, cooperative, hard worker

Your Turn! Work with a partner and brainstorm as many qualities as you can think of.

Compare your list with Top Ten Qualities of an Effective Team Player (next page).

Personal Reflection: Working with Others

The ability to work with others on a team is an important skill to have for any job. Questions for consideration:

1. List up to five individuals with whom you believe you should partner on a sustained basis. _____

_____

_____

2. Make a list of three instances you have observed recently that you know need to be addressed to build relationships.

_____

_____

3. How can you get the most from your partnering? _____

_____

_____

4. How do you fit in when building relationships every day?

_____

_____

5. What would others say is your greatest strength as a partner?

_____

_____

6. When was the last time the team went offsite to conduct team building? What were the advantages and challenges of this activity? _____

_____

_____

Self-Assessment: Working with Others

Fill in the chart below to evaluate your skill in working with others.

I can...	Yes	Somewhat	No
Treat people fairly, while recognizing different people have different needs.			
Work co-operatively with a partner or team to complete tasks.			
Coordinate my work with my colleagues to complete group projects.			
Name three non-work-related facts about everyone on the team (i.e., hobbies, kids, interests).			
Complete my assigned work on time so that team deadlines are met.			
Complete my fair share of tasks when working with a partner or team.			
Initiate conversations and take first steps to get to know others better.			
Follow directions from my partner or team members as required.			
Give directions to my partner or team members as required.			
Participate in making group decisions by contributing my ideas and suggestions.			
Contribute to making decisions co-operatively and settling differences respectfully.			

I can...	Yes	Somewhat	No
Improve my work based on suggestions and advice I receive from my partner or other team members.			
Listen without judgement.			
Understand other people and where they come from.			
Share personal, authentic aspects of myself.			

Look at the "Yes" columns in the "Working with Others Self-Assessment" to identify your strengths and record them below. Next, look at the "Somewhat" and/or "No" columns to identify the areas that you need to develop or strengthen and record them below.

Strengths:

1. _____

2. _____

3. _____

4. _____

5. _____

6. _____

7. _____

8. _____

Room for Improvement:

1. _____

2. _____

3. _____

4. _____

5. _____

6. _____

7. _____

8. _____

CHAPTER 7

TALENT MANAGEMENT

When the experienced employee walks out the door, they take with them not only their own personal talent that they were diligently expending to complete their assigned tasks, but also their accumulated wisdom and experience, which was gained while working for the employing organization. Rothwell (2010) observes the "chronic crisis of governance," evidenced by high personnel turnover, loss of confidence in leaders, and rampant scandals stemming from organizational misconduct plaguing every sector of industry.

Here is a passage from my business journal. It illustrates how I applied Talent Management thinking in my company's infancy to ensure long term success in my business:

> "As a business owner, of a micro-company poised on the brink of global expansion (currently, I am the only full-time employee), I find it highly valuable to have established my own Succession Plan, which allows me to ensure continuity of operations, talent development, and professional growth and grooming. Each of these is a key part of my business Human Resources Plan. It is

easier to start with the basics and expand than to cre-ate a product as a reactive response to a company that has grown without a plan. I can use developed assess-ments and processes to assist staff once I start hiring personnel."

As CEO and employee, I have utilized two key assessments. First, I used the Identifying Skills Requirement Worksheet to see what talents I would need to bring aboard to develop a strong and talented team. Next, I used the Talent Man-agement Self-Assessment to identify areas where I needed to improve my level of competence. It helped me to lay out the plan for growing and expanding my practice, much like I would do if I were an employee of the organization. It helped me to identify actions that would ensure my suc-cess, as well as skill sets and training that would eventually aid me in my professional pursuits. I found that each tool could be very easily modified and used for new partners and employees, as well as utilization to provide clear guid-ance as a hiring and interview tool.

While these measures may seem simplistic, there is an abun-dance of research out there that supports the benefits and good will built when employees know you have a plan for them. It is through these small measures that we begin to clearly communicate, "I make sure you win!" Xavier (2005) challenges leaders to become more adaptable to the point of being fluid; this is a standard requirement for being able to stay ahead of ever-changing circumstances that are part of the new service-centered and customer-focused market environment. Managers must begin looking in unusual places for solutions to human resource challenges. We must be ready to grow our talent management strategies and solutions playbook by creating new pages that may not be commonly accepted and are at times risky. Lastly, we must learn to lead differently, expanding broader than we ever have in the past to be more inclusive with our people, more transparent in our processes, and more decisive in making hard decisions that will ultimately ensure our organizations continue moving forward.

Talent managers must be ready for every twist of fate. As stated earlier, they must be more dynamic and adaptive than they ever have been in the past. Ulrich et al (2005) note that although many human resource experts anticipate that there will be a global personnel shortage, these forecasts are grounded in the assumptions that people will leave the workforce in mass quantities once they reach retirement-eligible age. However, research shows this is not that case. Older workers are staying in the workforce longer and experiencing success. This group demonstrated remarkable tenacity in attaining jobs during the Great Recession (December 2007 to June 2009). During this period, while younger workers (age sixteen to twenty-four years old) and prime working age adults (age twenty-four to fifty-four years old) experienced a 13% and 7% decline in employment respectively, many older workers entered the workforce and increased their overall presence by 7.6% (Fogg et al, 2012).

So how might innovative and resourceful talent managers make themselves ready to capitalize on opportunities that the aging workforce that is not ready to retire might present? As the ever-aging workforce expands in coming years, there is an opportunity to find ways to address the realities and alleviate the stereotypes and challenges associated with aging, we are in a much better position to address other stereotypes associated with common cultural landmines, such as race, gender, religion, and sexual orientation.

Human resource experts who see these developments as opportunities are building an even greater appreciation for the unique contributions of employees who bring their talents each day to create the solutions of the future. Aust et al (2015) observe that Human Resource Management (HRM) must be deployed differently, in a way that focuses on scholarship and determining what the optimal conditions are to encourage high performance through internal and external alignment of the HR function, while being appropriate for HR strategy with organization strategy.

Further investment in the development of suitable and user-friendly Talent Management Models is an essential step in improving talent management within organizations. Han and Boulay (2013) tout a new talent management model which links key approaches to learning, individual performance, and organizational performance. Although this model is complex and requires a significant investment in data collection, they believe it to be a key component in improving evaluation of environments conducive to full potential fulfillment with employees.

Introducing Talent Management Tools and Exercises

Using this section's worksheet, assessment, and activity establishes a solid foundation for successful talent management interventions. These resources will help leaders take an objective inventory of their skills in this area and identify areas of both strength and necessary improvement. They will also help leaders and teams to think through often-overlooked openings where their attention and efforts could be of greatest impact. Use these tools to evaluate current talent management efforts and take them to the next level!!

Worksheet: Identifying Skills Requirements

Instructions: Use this form to list the actual skills you'll need to ensure team success in its assignment. Next, use the second set of questions to help you refine how to choose the right people with the right skills for your team or organization.

1. What skills are required to complete the tasks assigned?

_____

_____

_____

2. Where will the people come to complete the tasks?

_____

_____

_____

3. How do you want to organize the people working on the project? (this impacts whether you need supervisory personnel!)

_____

_____

_____

_____

_____

_____

Use a structured approach relating to your talent and skill set needs.

1. Is there a specific skill or combination of skills required to complete this task? _____

_____

_____

_____

_____

_____

2. How much experience should the person/people have to complete this task? _____

_____

_____

_____

_____

_____

3. Does a person need to have specific experience doing this task, or can general experience be applied? If so, what general experience is required? _____

_____

_____

_____

_____

4. In addition to technical skills, are there any specific interpersonal skills required to complete this task competently and effectively, such as good written or verbal communication skills, negotiating or diplomacy skills, management ability, or ability to speak a foreign language?

_____

_____

_____

_____

5. How many of these skilled people will be needed for each task, and how would they be organized by job title and job function?

_____

_____

_____

_____

Self-Assessment: Talent Management

Fill in the chart below to evaluate your skill in working with others.

	Yes	Not Sure	No
I can name five talents of several peers and of each person I lead.			
I make the best use of peoples' talents every day.			
I spend at least one hour each week learning about new ways to manage talent.			
I am aware of several organizational talent management resources.			
I have met with and discussed talent management with our organization's talent management lead.			
I help others achieve their career goals on a routine basis.			
I am considered a go-to person for developing others.			
I am actively mentoring one to two people right now.			
I have held a professional development conversation this week with a co-worker or someone who reports to me.			
My people get recognized for their hard work.			
I recognize the different motivational needs amongst all my personnel.			

	Yes	Not Sure	No
I am familiar with the processes for reprimand to engage direct reports in correcting lacking performance.			
I have been recognized within the organization as a lead developer of people.			
I know how to manage my teams to place people in roles where they can do what they do best.			
I easily use coaching in the development of my people.			
I have received formal training on talent management.			
I can show others how to build better balance where they are neither bored nor overwhelmed.			

Calculate your score!

3 points for Yes
2 points for Not Sure
0 points for No

Total = _____

Results

43- 51: You are a Talent Management Maestro! You are proficient at growing and developing people. Consider becoming a mentor to someone who is trying to develop in this area.

35- 43: You are on the journey with room for growth. Consider the areas identified in the survey and identify resources that can help you.

Below 35: You may want to prioritize efforts to create a personal development plan in this area. Consider hiring a coach or seeking mentorship or apprenticeship if you want to increase development in this area.

Activity: Identifying Talent Management Opportunities

The ability to develop others on a team is a critical leader-ship skill. Questions for consideration:

1. List up to five individuals with whom you believe you should engage in professional development discussions on a sustained basis.

_____

_____

_____

2. Make a list of items you have heard and seen recently that you know need to be addressed to build trusting relationships.

_____

_____

_____

3. How can you get the most from your people?

_____

_____

_____

4. How do you commit to developing people every day?

_____

_____

_____

5. What would others say is your greatest strength as a mentor?

_____

_____

_____

6. When was the last time the team went offsite to conduct professional development activities? What were the advantages and challenges of the endeavor?

_____

_____

_____

Chapter 8

ETHICAL INTERVENTIONS

In an "I make sure you win!' world, consultants recognize that their consulting talents are part of a calling and that each intervention is an opportunity to fully leverage their God-given talents for the benefit of the teams and the organizations they serve. Due to the inclusive nature of ethics, there is no limit to an individual's ethical growth. Mahatma Gandhi used the values of truth and non-violence to save India during periods of crisis in its values system. In a "lawless land" of borderless economies and under-regulated global markets, where the responsibility of the executive is greater than it has ever been, leaders and their teams can see that the entire organizational world is experiencing a crisis in its value system (Bansal and Bajpai, 2011).

Virtue does not just spontaneously occur; it is developed over time, through focused practice, intentional action, and persistent commitment to remaining true and authentic to your convictions. "Keeping the rules," as some might insist, does not serve as evidence of justification or salvation. Ethical beliefs are only abstract until they are challenged and proven. This primarily occurs through interactions external to the individual, whether it be in conversations with others, observing or discovering an unethical act, or reflecting on a situation and seeing it with fresh eyes, based on an ethical revelation that causes one to view a past action as unethical in hindsight.

A big factor in developing a successful ethical intervention is first recognizing the importance of building trust. Maister et al (2000) assert that having trust with customers can reap the benefits of closer bonds, and assurance that we are moving along the right path. He also notes that interactions that require the consultant to take a personal risk with a client are far more often reciprocated, thus increasing intimacy. And in true "faith without works is dead" fashion, Maister et al (2002) caution consultants on two types of risk they will encounter: the risk of doing the wrong thing, and the risk of not doing the right thing. He notes that oftentimes consultants are so paralyzed by the first that they unintentionally commit the second risk, to the detriment of client relationships.

Baldoni (2014) notes that we often think of trust in binary terms; either it exists within a leader, or it does not. Green, one of the co-authors of the Trusted Advisor, created an assessment tool that evaluates credibility (What has been said and how believable was it?), reliability (How dependable are you?), intimacy (How comfortable are people sharing with you?), and self-orientation (How much focus do you place on yourself compared to others?).

Maister (2000) appropriately observes that trust is not developed between people and institutions or people and processes. It exists between people and other people. Clear distinctions do exist.

Individual values tend to be instrumental: honesty, loyalty, patience, persistence, and consistency, all of which facilitate and enable goals. Meanwhile, organizational values tend to be more terminal: learning, aligned, strategic, responsive, and customer service oriented, all of which tend to focus on results and desired end state. Values are psychological in nature, based on individuals' experiences, beliefs, and perceptions. Organizations do not necessarily have values, yet they are a byproduct of human beings and the cultures they create. Therefore, it stands to reason that human beings impact organizational values and the directions and actions taken by the organization (Hultman, 2002).

Chapman (2011) notes that the Bible begins with a lesson on the complexities and perplexities related to trust dynamics. Genesis Chapters 1-2 tell the story of a benevolent creator who provides Adam and Eve with all things, so they want for not. There is only one thing they are asked to do: not eat from one tree of all the trees in the garden. Yet within two chapters of a fairly short interaction with the creator of the universe who offers everything, they are kicked out because of what can be argued is man's innate tendency towards distrust.

Poor values undermine the foundational well-being of organizations and society. Leaders who give into the temptations of greed tend to be uncompassionate and significantly lacking morals, standards, and inner fortitude (Ashta, 2014). More and more, what people do and carry out have no alignment with their internal values. Recent reports have documented managers tending to overlook unethical or borderline practices in an attempt to gain more power, money, or esteem, while ignoring trade-offs like lack of control, internal conflict, guilt, shame, decreased credibility, trust, and respect among followers. (Pruzan, 2008).

Teams and leaders of teams can proactively work together to establish ground rules for conduct. They can conduct training exercises where they learn more about the ethical implications that may result while engaged in various interventions. Witherington (2011) advises that before consultants engage in any sort of intervention that they ask themselves, "Will this work glorify God and edify other persons?" And, "Can it be an expression of love of God and love of neighbor?" Along those same lines, Bellman (2002) encourages consultants to find work that allows them to thrive, contribute to the world, make friends, and become the people they want to be.

If one is fortunate enough to work in the field of Management Consulting, the answer can be a resounding "Yes!" to both mandates. But it cannot happen without clarity and making decisions that are not always easy. Yet it is well worth it; having work that aligns with one's values and fulfills their purpose exemplifies the true definition of a successful consultant, making sure their clients, teams, and partners win.

Introducing Ethical Intervention Tools and Exercises

The exercises in this section will help leaders facilitate the critical conversations that will result in well-established guidelines for how they will interact and engage to truly benefit those who need their advocacy most. These exercises and tools work to bring to the conversation those uncomfortable topics such as bias, unproductive belief systems, and misaligned frameworks that threaten the good intentions of leaders and their teams. When it comes to ensuring ethical considerations are addressed, there is no substitute for transparency and clarity from the start.

Exercise: Establishing Team Code of Ethics

Thinking about potential ethical challenges is the key to addressing them properly once they arise. Questions for consideration:

1. What are the ethical considerations that your team must address?

_____

_____

_____

_____

_____

_____

_____

2. How are your team's ethical principles tied to its mission and goals?

_____

_____

_____

_____

_____

3. Describe the role and importance of the teams' ethical values.

_____

_____

_____

_____

_____

_____

4. What is the relationship between the organization's culture and the team's ethical decision-making philosophy?

_____

_____

_____

_____

_____

_____

5. How do you perceive the ethical climate?

_____

_____

_____

_____

_____

_____

_____

6. What are the primary ethical issues encountered?

_____

_____

_____

_____

_____

_____

7. What education is needed to help address ethical issues?

_____

_____

_____

_____

_____

_____

8. Are team members aware of current ethics-related policies, guidelines, and legislation within the organization and industry? Are additional policies or guidelines needed?

_____

_____

_____

_____

_____

9. What organizational ethics support services are available to staff and leaders?

_____

_____

_____

_____

_____

10. What educational strategies will be most effective to build staff capacity in the context of proper ethical conduct?

_____

_____

_____

_____

_____

_____

Establishing Teams Rules/Team Etiquette

Team Etiquette: Rules of acceptable personal behavior and courtesy when interacting with others in a social setting.

What are some of your team's rules for acceptable personal behavior? List as many as you think are necessary.

1.

_____

_____

2.

_____

_____

3.

_____

_____

4.

_____

_____

5.

_____

_____

6.

_____

_____

7.

_____

_____

Establishing Teams Rules/Team Etiquette (Cont'd)

Laws: A system of rules and punishments clearly defined and established by a group to maintain a safe and orderly work environment.

What are your team's primary governing principles to ensure safety and order? Again, list everything you think is appropriate.

1.

_____

_____

2.

_____

_____

3.

_____

_____

4.

_____

_____

5.

_____

_____

6.

_____

_____

7.

_____

_____

Profile of an "I Make Sure You Win"

When "I Make Sure You Win" is at the forefront of our intent, we recognize that our win is only a fragment of a bigger effort at play. When we assure our partners, supervisors, and direct reports that "I Make Sure You Win," it communicates our commitment to their success. Your win does not come at the detriment or sacrifice of someone else. Other parties don't lose. Relationships aren't damaged or irreparably harmed. It says, "My Win doesn't even count unless you win."

"I Make Sure You Win" is the part of us that has an easy way of connecting with various groups and types of people across ages, experiences, and competencies. When operating with this intention at the forefront, we tend to make it a point to get to know people and develop an understanding of their cultures, values, and beliefs (DeSilva, 2004). This spirit of conviction makes an appearance when leaders are mindful that they are in the privileged position to serve others as part of an organization's mission.

"I Will Make Sure You Win" looks at the vision and sees the future as if it's being projected onto a screen. This individual makes the hard calls of when to persevere or when to remove their foot from the gas and practice patience, when things are taking longer than expected. They constantly weigh the benefits and risks of initiatives and goals. They continuously navigate numerous internal conflicts,

modeling the behaviors of good leadership and steward-
ship of people. They balance leader development with good
partnering.

---

*"If you want to win in the 21st Century, you have to
empower others, making sure other people are
better off than you are."*   ~ Jack Ma

"I Make Sure You Win" is one of the most rewarding
aspects of the team member role, regardless of what your
position is on the team. We all have ample opportunities to
ensure that those around us feel supported, cared for, and
appreciated. Leaders operating from an "I Make Sure You
Win" stance exhibit the principles of partnering, and can
be found in every setting, grooming and encouraging new
talent. They make sure every intervention aligns with the
highest of ethical standards and embodies the proclama-
tion: "I MAKE SURE YOU WIN!"

PART III

WE ALL WIN!!!!

CHAPTER 9

STRATEGIC LEADERSHIP

Hughes and Beatty (2005) assert that a major challenge for leaders trying to shape healthy organizations is in understanding how to implement changes, so that they build progressively one upon each other. These changes are then more like evolution than contradictory actions that lack alignment, and cause confusion and frustration throughout the organization. The distinction that separates the strategic aspects of leadership is the requirement for the leader to take a long view of the process of shaping the organization's culture. This type of leader encourages the ongoing learning process of the organization by being clear on the key indicators and vision for the future. There must be alignment between the leader's talk and their actions. It benefits the organization and their teams for leaders to be inclusive in the development and assessment phases of the strategy making process. This facilitates shared understandings, optimizes synergies, and spurs buy-in from the group participating in strategy development. Leaders successfully guide their organizations through the organizational learning process, the means by which organizations evolve, grow, and respond to customer demands and the ever-changing market environment.

The organizational learning process includes the following five stages:

1. Initial Assessment
2. Internal Understanding
3. Setting a course
4. Acting on the course set, and
5. Marking progress

In identifying where the organization is in one of these phases, the leader and team can take actions to guide the organization through the current and follow-on phases. The leader is "the grand architect" in leading the organization and group to successful endeavors, in the opposite direction of "group think." Group think is especially risky for organizations that are trying to implement a learning cycle because multiple perspectives are needed in interpreting what divergent data may be telling the team, as well as when trying to determine the best next steps to take based on information and learning. If teams or groups of leaders fall into group think, all the best ideas might not be presented–or options supplied for discussion–resulting in the team's learning being limited to only a few obvious solutions, while more innovative, ingenious solutions fail to be introduced. The team's behavior, participation, and communication provide a great illustration of the organization's cultural forces at play. Leaders of organizations do not just make demands or requests. Leaders and managers within an organization represent those who have mastered fundamental elements of the culture's expectations. Their ability to make things happen can likely be attributed to their ability to engage more personnel, which is related to participation and communication amongst team members (Ackerman and Eden, 2012).

Cameron and Quinn (2011) point out that the challenge for the consultant coming into an organization (at the invitation of leaders) is that it is hard to identify and solve issues that were not to some degree linked to the leaders themselves. Leaders must be patient with their efforts to change or modify a culture. It is not an overnight turnaround, and efforts must be deliberate and measured to arrive at the desired outcomes. Leaders, on one hand, desire to shape and change culture, but on the other hand, once mature, culture will have a significant influence on those selected to lead. Leaders and culture are inextricably linked. The wise leader will employ great foresight when considering how measures taken today will blossom into the organization of tomorrow.

Strategic foresight can be an extremely powerful tool for leaders. It can be used personally by the leader to develop a vision of where they want their organization to go or as an empowerment tool to facilitate their teams looking beyond current environment constraints into where they need to be positioned and focused to capitalize on future opportunities (Cornish, 2007). While others are stuck in self-defeating rhetoric of "that's how it's always been done," those with foresight know a better future can only be found by those willing to envision a new path.

Thoms (1995) notes that over the past eighty years, leadership theories have evolved mainly around the premise that analysis and study of the past were the only means available for controlling the future. The author goes on to assert the existence of three categories of leader, based on their time-tense focus. There is the past-oriented leader, who tends to lean on past education, experiences, and relationships with followers to inform and influence their treatment and interactions of employees and team members. Next, there is the present-focused leader, who deals with the day-to-day taskings: the latest fire, the closest deadline, the neediest employees, and the most pressing issues on the mind of his or her boss. Lastly, there is the future-focused leader, who examines the work of today through a futurist's lens, anticipating the needs, visioning the organization's place in the future, forecasting opportunities, and preparing for potential challenges.

While all three perspectives are beneficial, most leaders are more comfortable with the past- and present-tense focus, signaling a need for greater development in future focused leadership. In the future, leadership will be far different than what we know today. Boundaries between internal and external people networks will blur, as organizations embrace the wisdom of crowds and the concept of a "global brain" to accomplish more than they ever thought possible. Through this pool of connectivity, cognition, and consciousness, strategic leaders have the potential to advance humanity beyond the limited confines of competitive systems, zero-sum games, and the breakdowns of social development.

Coates (2004) provides some additional clarification by offering several examples of leadership's trouble understanding time-orientation via the relay of real-world challenges faced while consulting. He notes that there are common problems in getting leaders to nail down a clear vision of the future and their organization's place in it. The author observes that many organizations refuse to make key explicit assumptions, simply based on their own processes, let alone assumptions about what their competition might be doing. The recurring theme is that the fear of the unknown results in a paralysis of actions essential to the organization's survival. Not only do leaders not know what the future holds, they feel they have no reliable resources to even venture a guess.

It is helpful to recognize that although there is much lip service to the contrary, many leaders will have reflexive reluctance to entering any future scenario, even one of their own making. This dilemma presents a prime opportunity for consultants and leaders willing to engage with decision makers and help them become more comfortable with making decisions and developing the strategies for their organization.

Additionally, it is important for leaders to self-assess and seek feedback from colleagues regarding strategic leadership development. Hughes and Beatty (2005) recommend utilizing Strength, Weakness, Opportunity and Threat (SWOT) analysis to assess one's own leadership development skill, much like one would evaluate organizations. They recommend using performance evaluations, instrument-based assessments, and boss and subordinate feedback to determine "where you are."

Self-assessment feeds the individual learning process. Additionally, self-assessment and insights from others whose opinions you value will assist in determining where you are, related to personal development goals and where you want to go. This process presents leaders with an opportunity to examine and validate their own core values and uncompromising truths, which define and distinguish them as leaders. Hughes and Beatty (2005) assert that strategic acting involves making decisions which forego immediate gratification for an alternative that offers greater future benefits. The clearer the vision, the easier it is to make the investments of time and energy that will result in long-term personal, spiritual, and professional success.

Introducing Strategic Leadership Tools and Exercises

This section's tools and exercises will help leaders assess their ability to tackle those highly complex problems that threaten the future of organizations. These challenging issues can't be resolved by a single command. They have causes that seem incomprehensible, solutions that seem uncertain, and they often require organizations to transform the way they do business. Every enterprise faces these kinds of challenges today.

These exercises and assessments will help leaders and teams to think through the way they bring people together for the benefit of the organization, and how well they lead teams to the solutions that keep the team going strong. These exercises can also help teams identify often overlooked prospects for collaboration and come together to solve issues that have far reaching risks and impacts.

Exercise: Consensus Building

Consensus is a decision-making process that ensures everyone agrees with the final decision. Work with a group of two to four people for this activity. You can do this with fellow learners or colleagues.

Directions: Read the scenario below and rank the items you think are most important to carry with you. Do this part on your own.

Part 1

It is late in the evening when you and two companions are on your way home in your motorboat. You suddenly hit a rock and your motor shuts off. You try everything to fix the motor, but you are unable to get it going. You have a smaller motor for emergencies, so you put it down and try to start it. It doesn't start. Nothing you or your companions do starts either motor. You decide to paddle to the nearest shore. Once you are on shore, you decide to hike to a nearby camp which is about fifteen miles away. Listed below are some items you have in the boat. What should you take with you? List them in order of importance.

1 – Most Important 16 – Least Important

_____ Bag of potato chips

_____ Bottled water, a four-pack

_____ CDs

_____ Camera

_____ Can of gasoline

_____ Compass

_____ Flares

_____ Hand tools: hammer, screwdriver, wrench

_____ Sleeping bag

_____ Fishing gear

_____ Fish that you caught

_____ Matches

_____ Pocket knife

_____ Portable boom box

_____ Ropes: one fifteen feet long and one twenty-five feet long

_____ Lake map

Part 2

You can carry only one item. Which items would you most like to take? List your top three choices.

1. _____

2. _____

3. _____

Part 3

Working in groups of three to seven, determine, as a group, the three items your group will carry. You are committed to the three you choose. But remember that each person can take only one item, and all three members must agree on the three items. Your group choices are:

1. _____

2. _____

3. _____

Part 4

1. Write your personal observations of what occurred in your group.

_____

_____

2. What did you learn about yourself in this activity? Did you fight for your choice?

_____

_____

3. Did you just agree with everyone else? Did you have lots to say? Or did you keep quiet?

_____

_____

Assessment: Team Make-Up Review

Team Name _____

Directions: Please respond to the survey items as they apply to your team's strategy making competency. For each item, check the appropriate response to demonstrate your agreement with what your team represents. This assessment can be used on teams ranging from four to twenty or more members.

5 – Strongly Agree   4 – Agree   3 – Neutral   2 – Disagree   1 – Strongly Disagree

	5	4	3	2	1
1. We assess our strengths and weaknesses often and with great honesty.					
2. We understand the threats and opportunities in the external environment.					
3. We possess a shared team vision of our future.					
4. We understand how our roles support the organizational mission.					
5. We keep current with technological, cultural, and market trends.					
6. We are clear about our basic purpose and core values.					
7. We think globally.					
8. We have few undiscussable subjects.					
9. We encourage others to improve by experimenting with varied approaches.					
10. We welcome different opinions.					
11. We are clear about what we WILL DO and what we WILL NOT DO.					

Assessment: Team Make-Up Review (Cont'd)

	5 – Strongly Agree	4 – Agree	3 – Neutral	2 – Disagree	1 – Strongly Disagree

12. We work well together.					
13. We are composed of diverse individuals with complementary talents.					
14. We share information well with each other.					
15. We have constructive interactions with others throughout the organization.					
16. We support professional growth and development.					
17. We advance based on performance, not politics.					
18. We effectively balance dealing with near- and long-term needs.					
19. We encourage an appropriate level of risk-taking.					
20. We do not waste our time or others' energy on unproductive practices.					
21. We respond effectively to opportunities and threats in the environment.					
22. We trust and respect each other.					
23. We foster cooperation rather than competition amongst units.					
24. We all share best practices between individuals and departments.					
25. We all exhibit high integrity.					
26. We are proud of the way we handle issues of right and wrong.					
27. We feel a positive sense of energy and excitement in our work.					

Self-Assessment: SWOT Analysis

Strengths

_____
_____
_____
_____
_____
_____
_____
_____
_____
_____
_____

Weaknesses

_____
_____
_____
_____
_____
_____
_____
_____
_____
_____
_____

Opportunities

_____
_____
_____
_____
_____
_____
_____
_____
_____
_____
_____

Threats

_____
_____
_____
_____
_____
_____
_____
_____
_____
_____
_____

Chapter 10

ORGANIZATIONAL DESIGN

Over the years, industry leaders have attempted to increase performance through branding, globalization, reverse-engineering of processes, new technologies... the list goes on and on. Amid these massive efforts, many ignored the key element to success: understanding and engaging with the culture. Organizational design offers a possible solution to wasted time and effort spent by leaders desiring greater alignment for their organizations. It entails taking intentional and strategic action around the shaping of traditional organizational structures, processes, and systems.

Burton, Obel, and Dasanctis (2011) describe misfits as any set of relations between the organizational goals, strategy type, environment, configuration, complexity, geographical distribution, knowledge exchange, task design, or people. Each dimension serves to better form the description of the organizational design, thus allowing for the visualization of relationships among all the design components.

Misfits between people can present significant issues and problems. Let's say we had an organization whose goals currently resulted in them being neither efficient, nor effective.

There are only a small number of people in the organization, but they are highly educated and skilled. The people and leaders involved might experience great friction due to a major misfit. The employees, who were "laboratory" oriented would find it extremely frustrating to work in an organization that did not present them with opportunities to encounter and resolve challenges. This is because the organization has no clear direction, and no environmental factors to spur the organization towards change.

Misfits often end up in manager information overload – overwhelming demands placed on the department's knowledge processing capacity. The results of this include delayed decisions, actions, and outcomes. The alignment of dimensions ensures that teams have capable structures in place to provide the capacity to support knowledge requirements.

In *Organizational Culture and Leadership* (2010), Schein instructs organizational leaders to implement small changes to better facilitate advancing their organizations' cultures. He offers this as a far better option than attempting a complete overhaul approach, noting the importance of understanding and accepting the current organizational culture as is, and not trying to impose one's own version of what they think their organization's culture should look like. Instead of looking for things that are "wrong" with culture, it may be a far more productive venture to look for situations that lack alignment and congruence to the culture.

Chermack (2011) avers that truly great companies, those with long-standing high performance and sustained reputations for excellence in their industries, have the foresight and innovation to change the environment and be the pacesetters for their industries. Although foresight does provide an obvious competitive advantage, it differs from other competitive leverage tools in that it is less about finding or having information, resources, or capabilities that no one else has, and more about understanding and utilizing resources in ways that are more adaptive and creative than others within the industry (Hines, 2011). This line of thinking is supported by Slaughter (1993), who notes that the premise of today's thinking is that resources are limited and also that we as humans have the right to use any and all available resources to our benefit, regardless of future detrimental impacts it may have on other species, cultures, and races. To free up leaders' thinking about the future, it is more productive to focus on resourcefulness over limited resources. Further, they should be considerate of sustainable outcomes with solutions that ensure an even brighter future, versus leaving the future (and future leaders) to live with the consequences of short-sighted activities.

Hollinger (2012) suggests greater focus on meeting the needs of the customers to identify opportunities for gaining a competitive advantage through effective design initiatives. The author goes on to note that oftentimes organizations suffer from "cross-functional pollution." This can be organizational strategies not being fully thought out and/or structures and technologies put in place without proper supporting systems and training for staff. These are opportunities where strong leadership presence and greater engagement of all are affected by key organizational changes. With thoughtful planning and consideration of alignment and structure, leaders can make sure that "We all win."

Introducing Organizational Design Tools and Exercises

As a leader who has likely observed or had first-hand experience with the effects of globalization and economic crisis, you are probably well acquainted with the mandate to constantly assess and adapt how teams, departments, branches, and divisions are configured. Global and industry influences have forced organizations to rethink their strategies and change the way they operate.

In this section, leaders will find tools and exercises that will empower them to appraise their proficiency in effectively organizing and arranging teams for maximum effectiveness. These tools and exercises are perfect for spurring conversations about what leaders hold most important for delivering consistent, high-quality products, services, and results to customers.

Exercise: Roles Within Teams

Choose three to four team roles that you are interested in, based on your assessment of your own strengths. Create a list of tasks that someone in the role might need to do in relation to working with others.

Role 1: _____

Working with Others' Tasks

1. _____
2. _____
3. _____
4. _____
5. _____

Why is it important that a person in this role work as a team member?

_____

_____

Role: _____

Working with Others' Tasks

1. _____
2. _____
3. _____
4. _____
5. _____

Exercise: Roles Within Teams (Cont'd)

Why is it important that a person in this role work as a team member?

_____

Role 3: _____

Working with Others' Tasks

1. _____
2. _____
3. _____
4. _____
5. _____

Why is it important that a person in this role work as a team member?

_____

Role 4: _____

Working with Others' Tasks

1. _____
2. _____
3. _____
4. _____
5. _____

Why is it important that a person in this role work as a team member?

_____

_____

Exercise: Assessing Your Organization's Design*

As a team, review, discuss, and determine the appropriate multi-dimensional contexts (structural and human components) of your organization. Definitions associated with the various aspects of your organization's design are defined below.

Organization Goals – Where the organization is and wants to be

- ⊕ None
- ⊕ Efficiency – Focus on inputs, processes, and costs
- ⊕ Effectiveness – Focus on outputs, products, and revenues
- ⊕ Both

Dimension – Overarching approach or method selected

- ⊕ None
- ⊕ Explore – Focus on variation, risk taking, and innovation
- ⊕ Exploit – Focus on refinement, efficiency, and implementing
- ⊕ Various

Strategy – Endgame focus

- ⊕ React – Low in both exploration and exploitation
- ⊕ Defend – Low exploration and high exploitation
- ⊕ Prospect – High exploration and low exploitation
- ⊕ Analyzer – High in both exploration and exploitation
  - with Innovation – leans toward defending
  - without Innovation – leans toward prospecting

Exercise: Assessing Your Organization's Design* (Cont'd)

Environment – External factors requiring response
- ⊕ Calm – Low complexity, high predictability
- ⊕ Varied – High complexity, high predictability
- ⊕ Locally Stormy – Low complexity, low predictability
- ⊕ Turbulent – High complexity, low predictability

Configuration – Organization structure (Org Chart)
- ⊕ Simple – Low effectiveness, low function
- ⊕ Functional – Low effectiveness, highly functional
- ⊕ Divisional – Highly effective, low specialization
- ⊕ Matrix – Highly effective and specialized in function

Organizational Complexity – Operational differentiation
- ⊕ Blob – Low horizontal and vertical
- ⊕ Tall – Low horizontal, high vertical
- ⊕ Flat – High horizontal, low vertical
- ⊕ Symmetric – High horizontal and vertical

Knowledge Exchange – Communications practices
- ⊕ Informal – Low integration, low technology
- ⊕ Formal – High integration, low technology
- ⊕ Cellular – Low integration, high technology
- ⊕ Network – High integration, high technology

Exercise: Assessing Your Organization's Design* (Cont'd)

Task Design – Primary mode of performance

⊕ Orderly – Highly divisible, highly repetitive

⊕ Complicated – Low divisibility, highly repetitive

⊕ Fragmented – Highly divisible, low repetition

⊕ Knotty – Neither divisible or repetitive

People – Skills, training, and professional acumen

⊕ Shop – Low number, low professionalization

⊕ Factory – High number, low professionalization

⊕ Laboratory – Low number, high professionalization

⊕ Office – High number, high professionalization

Leadership – Preferred way of leading people

⊕ Maestro – Low delegation, highly predictable work

⊕ Manager – Low delegation, low predictability

⊕ Leader – High delegation, highly predictable work

⊕ Producer – High delegation, low predictability

Organizational Climate_- Emotional processing

⊕ Group – Low change readiness, low tension

⊕ Internal Process – Low change readiness, high tension

⊕ Developing – High change readiness, low tension

⊕ Rational – High change readiness, high tension

Exercise: Assessing Your Organization's Design* (Cont'd)

Coordination and Control – Means of ensuring quality

- Family – Informal process, centralized audits
- Machine – Formal process, centralized audits
- Market – Informal process, decentralized audits
- Clan/Mosaic – Formal process, decentralized audits

Information Systems – Data processing capacity

- Event Driven – Small data load, low tacit knowledge
- Data Driven – Large data load, low tacit knowledge
- People Driven – Small data load, highly tacit
- Relationship Driven – Large data load, highly tacit

Incentives – Means of encouraging desired action/behavior

- Personal – Low focus on results, high on compliance
- Skill – Low focus on results, high focus on skill/role
- Bonus – High focus on results and individual effort
- Profit – High focus on results and team effort

*Adapted from Burton, R.M., Obel, B. and Desanctis, G. (2011). *Organizational Design: A step-by-step approach*. Melbourne, NY: Cambridge University Press.

Quick Reference: Organizational Design Space Chart*

Design	A	B	C	D
Organization Goals	None	Efficiency	Effective	Both
Dimension	None	Exploit	Explore	Various
Strategy	React	Defend	Prospect	Analyzer with or without Innovation
Environment	Calm	Varied	Locally Stormy	Turbulent
Configuration	Simple	Functional	Divisional	Matrix
Organizational Complexity	Blob	Tall	Flat	Symmetric
Knowledge Exchange	Informal	Formal	Cellular	Network
Task Design	Orderly	Complicated	Fragmented	Knotty
People	Shop	Factory	Laboratory	Office
Leadership	Maestro	Manager	Leader	Producer
Organizational Climate	Group	Internal Process	Developing	Rational
Coordination and Control	Family	Machine	Market	Clan/Mosaic
Information Systems	Event Driven	Data Driven	People Driven	Relationship Driven
Incentives	Personal	Skill	Bonus	Profit

*Adapted from Burton, R.M., Obel, B. and Desanctis, G. (2011). *Organizational Design: A step-by-step approach*. Melbourne, NY: Cambridge University Press.

CHAPTER 11

LEADERSHIP ANALYTICS

In the mid-1930s Britain's Science Fiction Association began publishing a magazine called *Tomorrow: The Magazine of the Future*, with H.G. Wells as its prophet. The magazine provided its readers with predictions of coming technological developments. Unfortunately, only a few issues were published before its editors and writers had to march off to World War II. However, during its brief existence, it was extremely provocative, particularly in the realm of data analytics. In the Spring, 1938 issue, Professor A.M. Low suggested that Britain should have a Minister for the Future, who would collect data from all over the world to tabulate, correlate, compare and calculate. Low noted that this minister should be "Like a spider sitting in a web," drawing in all knowledge, and working out—on scientific lines—the effect that the latest developments and discoveries would probably have on the human race (Cornish, 2005).

Eighty-five years later, we are still looking for our own Ministers of the Future, and so far, data scientists seem to be our answer. Are data scientists the answer to bringing all the business leaders, key stakeholders, management teams data miners and analysts together into one dynamic and productive conversation? Paredes (2015) seems to think so, noting, that a skilled data scientist is someone who demonstrates a strong appreciation for what technology can bring to bear; he or she knows what analytics are available and possible, and most important, has excellent communication skills.

Data scientists are using analytics to enable the rapid extraction, transformation, loading, search, analysis, and sharing of massive data sets. By analyzing a large, integrated, real-time database, rather than smaller, independent, batch-processed data sets, they hope to quickly identify previously unseen correlations and patterns to better inform organizational leaders' decision making. Although related to traditional Database Management and Business Intelligence systems, Data Analytics dramatically accelerate the ability to process data in terms of volume, velocity, variety, and variability of data.

The results from this support help managers to better measure and provide oversight to the most critical functions of their businesses. Companies start by identifying significant business opportunities that may be enhanced by superior data, and then determine whether data analysis solutions are needed. If they are, then there is a need to acquire or develop the hardware, software, and talent needed to capitalize on the opportunity. This often requires the addition of data scientists who are skilled in programming the right questions, identifying cost-effective information sources, finding true patterns of causality, and translating analytic insights into actionable information.

Considering these extraordinary advances, it can be tempting for leaders to rely on purely data-driven answers to make complex decisions for their organizations. But data experts caution against this course of action, asserting that leadership is the single greatest determinant as to how analytical an organization will be. Santaferraro (2013) relays how business leaders are now learning so much about the benefits and limitations of what the power of analytics can offer over their previous dependence on hunch and intuition. However, hunch and intuition can never be fully replaced by data analytics. There will always be a place for leaders to leverage experience and an understanding of their trade that goes beyond pure analytics.

Pfeffer and Sutton (2000) caution that measurement tools cannot be so influential in guiding people's decisions that important elements of behavior and performance are not given proper consideration. It can be risky when leaders who place too much emphasis on measurements are given too much or too little because of this relentless focus. Measurements are not perfect, and without a dose of intuition, they can spell disaster as quickly as if no measurements were used.

To ensure "We All Win," organizations will have to take an intentional stance to change their culture. Schein (2010) observes the essence of a group's culture is its pattern of shared, basic taken-for-granted assumptions. The culture will manifest itself at the level of observable artifacts and shared espoused values, norms, and rules of behavior. Leading analytics can support this, but it still comes back to highly connected human systems at work.

Introducing Leadership Analytics Tools and Exercises

Using this section's tools and exercises will help leaders assess standing in how well they leverage the opportunities that collecting and assessing data presents and explore options for ensuring the successful implementation of data. These exercises will assist leaders as they uncover surprising insights that could lead to unexpected new program or product ideas. Use the framework to facilitate a discussion amongst leaders that will support them in taking quick action and decisively determine the data-driven ambitions of the enterprise, setting the scope of the endeavor, and actively leading the charge into the pursuit of data-driven decision making.

These exercises can also help executives identify often-overlooked opportunities to apply leadership analytics. Moreover, these exercises will assist in determining the best candidate to work with diverse audiences and constituencies throughout the organization, someone who will welcome insight and dialogue for better data leveraging for organizational benefit.

Step-By-Step: Implementing Data Analytics

Step 1: Select a pilot. Select a team, business unit, or work group with a compelling opportunity to capitalize on big data analytics.

Notes: _____

_____

_____

Step 2: Bring together the Big Data subject matter experts. Establish a leadership group and team of data scientists with the skills and resources necessary to drive the effort successfully.

Notes: _____

_____

_____

Step 3: Identify best opportunities. Determine the specific decisions and actions that can be improved through the implementation of Big Data.

Notes: _____

_____

_____

Step 4: Decide on data solutions. Select the most appropriate hardware and software solutions for the targeted decisions.

Notes: _____

_____

_____

Step 5: Elect level of investment. Decide to purchase or rent the system.

Notes: _____

_____

_____

Step 6: Institute governance. Develop guiding principles, such as data privacy and security policies.

Notes: _____

_____

_____

Step 7: Testing. Test, learn, share, and refine.

Notes: _____

_____

_____

Step 8: Institutionalize. Develop repeatable models and expand applications to additional business areas.

Notes: _____

_____

_____

Framework: A Data Analytics Planning Framework

Two primary considerations will drive the way your organization approaches data analytics:

1. The clarity around the organization's objectives and goals, and

2. The organizational capacity available to implement and apply leadership analytics approaches.

See the grid below and use it to determine and discuss where your organization falls and what is practical in introducing leadership analytics to teams.

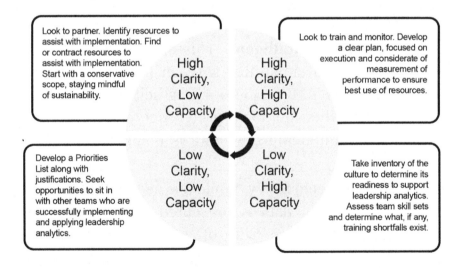

Look to partner. Identify resources to assist with implementation. Find or contract resources to assist with implementation. Start with a conservative scope, staying mindful of sustainability.

High Clarity, Low Capacity

Look to train and monitor. Develop a clear plan, focused on execution and considerate of measurement of performance to ensure best use of resources.

High Clarity, High Capacity

Low Clarity, Low Capacity

Develop a Priorities List along with justifications. Seek opportunities to sit in with other teams who are successfully implementing and applying leadership analytics.

Low Clarity, High Capacity

Take inventory of the culture to determine its readiness to support leadership analytics. Assess team skill sets and determine what, if any, training shortfalls exist.

Tips for Success: Selecting the Right "Champion" to Usher in Leadership Analytics

Below, you will find some of the key characteristics that will help you in identifying the ideal Leadership Analytics Champion within your organization.

Characteristics of the Ideal Leadership Analytics Champion:

- **Excellent Story Teller**. It is imperative that this individual can "tell the story" of what the data suggests in a way that is meaningful, relevant, and responsive to the specific data needed in a particular circumstance. Data should tell the audience: " What?" "So What?" and "What Next?"

- **Emotionally Intelligent**. This speaks to the critical ability to empathize with an individual's information needs. It requires being self-aware enough to know when personal preference or bias may be unduly influencing how data is being percieved or presented.

- **Technical (tech) Savvy**. While one section of the audience to whom data is presented might accept the information at face value, others will want to understand the processes and steps by which the data was collected. Being able to present these steps in a way that is repeatable, reliable, and well vetted is a necessary skill set.

- **Systems of System Mindset**. It is all related. It is crucial to see connections and implications around what seem to be independent and divergent pieces of data. Think in terms of divergent and convergent data, comparisons and contrasts, and how shifting one aspect of bundled assumptions creates a kaleidoscope of new considerations, impacts, and opportunities.

CHAPTER 12

GLOBAL CONSULTING

Consulting is essential to organizational development. Organizational development supports business strategy by playing a key role in helping organizations change themselves. It assists organizations in assessing themselves and their environments and revitalizing their structures and processes for continued success. This process has strong implications for the global consultant in that they are often brought in when leaders identify the need for assessment, change, or solutions to solve complex problems (Cummings and Worley, 2015).

Critical elements of a planned intervention include defining an action plan, gaining commitment, and using collected information to guide how change is implemented. Global consultants apply their knowledge of planned changes, the action research model, and positive methodologies to change management. While these tidbits are all ways in which consultants deliver value added, the most essential piece of information the global consultant must figure out is how their role is directly aligned with the needs of the organization. Consultants are hired to provide a specific expertise that is unavailable internally. They often offer an unbiased, new perspective, which aids the business in continuing its learning and evolutionary process. Sometimes by their mere presence alone, the global consultant can signal new shifts in power, focus, and strategic direction (Cummings and Worley, 2015).

A planned organizational intervention normally includes all the steps of the Action Research Model (ARM), the standard process used in organizational change. Through Action Research, the global consultant begins to understand the system in which they are involved, and the client group begins to take responsibility for the system in which they live. Action Research is problem centered, client centered, and action oriented. Steps in the Action Research model include entry, contracting, data gathering and diagnosis, feedback, action planning, selecting, and implementing an intervention and post implementation evaluation (Cummings and Worley, 2009).

Davila et al (2013) recommend that organizations seeking to create an environment where innovation thrives must have clarity and alignment around their innovation strategy. Signs of this include an innovation program that is measured, focused, recognized, and communicated clearly, and complemented by appropriate rewards linked to performance. The authors also caution that innovations are not to be viewed independently but must be considered in terms of market potential. They advise that leaders consider the following options when valuing an innovation's potential:

- Product and services – Consumers purchase because of perceived improvement.

- Process Innovation – Often invisible to the consumer, but vital to cost capitation and profits.
- Enabling Innovation – Any catalyst that helps the company to execute its innovation strategy faster.

The largest barrier to successfully implementing change within organizations is the lack of fit between leadership's stated strategies and the organization's structures, systems, and culture. To this end, global consultants can help leaders adeptly navigate a complex, intricate, and ever-changing global landscape. This requires a great deal of cultural agility. Caligiuri (2012) defines cultural agility as the ability to modify one's social alignment rapidly and accurately without losing balance. Unfortunately, cultural agility is a competency that few global leaders possess, and even fewer master; it is built by combining individual skills and abilities, motivation, and experience. With continuous orientation and by developing global consultants with high cultural agility acumen, we can do our part to ensure the next generation of consultants and the organizations they serve will win!

Introducing Global Consulting Tools and Exercises

The template and quick references in this section will help leaders facilitate the streamlining of their organizations, by guiding the activities that will enable them to come up with the strategies to optimize operations. Let these instruments move you in the right direction towards transforming your organization and setting the bars high for achievement and performance.

These exercises may be applied to assess the organization's current challenges and develop proposals to advise executives. Ultimately, this will help them to resolve pressing operational problems. Use these tools to conduct internal observations that will help the organization identify the best strategies to grow profits and productivity. It can be a real game-changer to recommend the right organizational changes after analyzing problems and successfully monitoring their implementation, without the assistance of external consultants! At the very least, leaders seeking solutions to their challenges can appreciate the process and general approach that global consulting services take.

Template: A Sample Methodology

The first step in the methodology of this sample consultation is to determine the need by asking several questions to gain clarity about the problem. From these questions and the resulting discussion, we developed an organizational needs statement. The organizational need statement was, "We want to have better team harmony and better team building. We want people to respect and treat each other well."

In step two, we decided that we needed more insights and input about the state of the current culture, as well as thoughts about what the preferred culture would look like.

For this requirement, we selected several members within the organization to participate in the Organizational Culture Assessment Instrument (OCAI) workshop. During this workshop, we provided background on the OCAI, relaying that it is an extremely popular and effective measure for determining organizational culture, as well as identifying the gap between the organization's current culture and the culture that will make the organization extremely successful into the future.

Next, after reviewing the findings from the OCAI, we discussed possible solutions to the organizational needs statement, which included an exploration of activities with the potential to increase team harmony and enhance team development. One of the solutions discussed was putting on a conflict resolution workshop to help team members better communicate and get past interpersonal conflicts encountered at work. Another solution was placing greater emphasis on

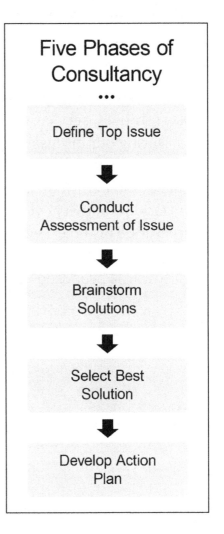

Five Phases of Consultancy
•••

Define Top Issue

⬇

Conduct Assessment of Issue

⬇

Brainstorm Solutions

⬇

Select Best Solution

⬇

Develop Action Plan

educating staff more about the organization's mission in order to rally and solidify members behind a common goal.

Following identification of potential solutions, we worked with leaders to determine which solution the organization was most likely to pursue. As a first step, it was determined that we should develop a project called "Creating Harmony and An Environment of Trust and Respect" in pursuit of the goal to put on a conflict resolution workshop.

Then, we developed a plan of action, outlining work phases/ stages to completion, milestones/activities, deliverables (product, service, or result) and deadlines/due dates. During our discussions, we outlined who would be responsible for key deliverables, identified resources and shortfalls, and determined timelines in the context of the organizational activity cycle and the meeting of the board of directors. This board would review our proposals, determine priorities in implementation, and decide how much to invest towards proposed initiatives.

Quick Reference: Organizational Cultural Inventory

Cameron and Quinn (2011) aver that culture defines the core values, assumptions, interpretations, and approaches characteristic to an organization. The authors developed the Competing Values Framework (CVF) to identify significant aspects of organizational design in order to determine where an organization is within its learning cycle. The Framework also serves to build understandings around organizational qualities, theories of effectiveness, human resource management roles, and management skill sets. The CVF has been shown to display a high degree of accuracy in reflecting well-known and widely accepted categorical schemes of how people think, their values and assumptions, and how they process information.

The tool for collecting data for the CVF is the Organizational Culture Assessment Instrument (OCAI). It allows us to diagnose the orientation of cultural strength, type, and congruence (Cameron and Quinn, 2011). Within the Competing Values Framework, four core values emerge. They are: Clan, Adhocracy, Market, and Hierarchy. Each of these four values represents opposing and competing values on an internal versus external, and flexibility versus stability spectrum.

Culture Type: CLAN

Orientation: COLLABORATE

Leader Type: Facilitator, Mentor, Teambuilder

Value Drivers: Commitment, Communications, Development

Theory of Effectiveness: Human development and high commitment produce effectiveness

Culture Type: ADHOCRACY

Orientation: CREATE

Leader Type: Innovator, Entrepreneur, Visionary

Value Drivers: Innovative Outputs, Transformation, Agility

Theory of Effectiveness: Innovativeness, vision, and constant change produce effectiveness

Culture Type: HIERARCHY

Orientation: CONTROL

Leader Type: Coordinator, Monitor, Organizer

Value Drivers: Efficiency, Timeliness, Consistency, Uniformity

Theory of Effectiveness: Control and efficiency with capable processes produce effectiveness

Culture Type: MARKET

Orientation: COMPETE

Leader Type: Hard driver, Competitor, Producer

Value Drivers: Market share, Goal achevement, Profitability

Theory of Effectiveness: Aggressive competition and customer emphasis produce effectiveness

Figure 4. Adapted illustration based on Cameron and Quinn's Competing Values Framework

Assessment: Rate Yourself as a Solver of Problems

Are you a good problem solver? Use this checklist to rate your problem-solving skills. Read each sentence. Put a check in the column that best describes how often you do what each sentence says. Circle the number of the items that you have checked "never" or "unsure." The circled items are skills you need to learn and use.

Problem-Solving Skill	Always	Some times	Rarely	Never	Unsure
I try to find out as much as I can about a problem before trying to solve it.					
To get information, I talk to others who may be familiar with this type of problem.					
I consult printed or visual resources, such as trade journals and trouble-shooting guides when trying to solve a problem.					
I go on the Internet and research the problem to see how other people may have dealt with this type of problem.					

Problem-Solving Skill	Always	Some times	Rarely	Never	Unsure
I list possible solutions to a problem before choosing one.					
I try to judge how well a solution is suited to a problem before trying it.					
I consider safety precautions and warnings when solving a problem.					
I conduct a test or dry run of a solution before carrying it out.					
When recommending a solution, I describe the problem, a solution, and its advantages and disadvantages.					

Step-By-Step: Conducting an Intervention

Problem Case: You're a new member to a team. Over your first month onboard, you notice some concerning characteristics demonstrated by team members. The behaviors seem to result in the team continuously failing to meet deadlines and team agreements on how team members have agreed to work together. Your team is having a monthly check-in meeting. Use the prompt below to map out how you might bring the specific observation to the team's attention for discussion, reflection, and resolution.

1. Identify the observed behavior, or matter of concern; be clear and specific.

_____

_____

_____

2. Provide examples of how specific behaviors, potential risks, or negativity impact team-shared goals.

_____

_____

_____

3. List possible solutions, focusing on shared goals and a vision of what the team believes it can be and what it can achieve.

_____

_____

_____

4. Evaluate possible results of each potential solution.

_____

_____

_____

5. Decide on the best solution or prioritize and sequence a set of potential solutions for implementation and integration into a team development plan (much like an individual development plan but for the entire team).

_____

_____

_____

Profile of a "We All Win"

When operating from your inner "We All Win," you are demonstrating your highest levels of leader influence and impact. The confidence confirmed from "I Win" is fully developed and you've evolved that into demonstrated relationships where you put the well-being of others at the same importance as your personal goals and aspirations. You have mastered the skill of coming up with resourceful and sustainable solutions that benefit all parties. At this point, you have the "team of teams"; the entire organization can go forth together into whatever the future holds. There is an essential will shared by all to commit to whole culture's success, to personal growth, and to feel a connection with the organization's success over individual preferences.

Leaders feel ready to assume the role of transformational leader by:

1. raising team members' consciousness
2. getting team members to act past their own self-interest, and
3. motivating team members to attain higher-level needs.

> *"If you and your team are willing to do what it takes, you can build and sustain an incredibly strong culture of trust and performance and accomplish remarkable things."*
> ~ Mike Robbins

In a "We All Win!" world, leaders understand and can clearly conceptualize a vision for the organizations. Major aspects of the vision are often strategic. They can clearly articulate the amazing future (step 1). But often, this is at the expense of giving up past belief systems that no longer serve the entire group (step 2). This can cause many to fall outside their comfort zone, possibly requiring new organizational structuring. Especially with long standing, well-established entities, leaders must speak to the deeper team ambition to achieve even greater feats (step 3). They need to look beyond the comfort zone and status quo and recognize the prospects that await. Through acts of team trust and the ability to see the strategic, leaders demonstrate what it takes to ensure the next generation of leaders and a healthy culture for years to come; therefore, "We All Win!!"

CHAPTER 13

NEXT SUCCESS STEPS:
BRINGING IT ALL TOGETHER

Every problem that faces organizations today and well into the future can be addressed. They can be solved, made less daunting and much more palatable if leaders enter into their engagement with a Three Win mindset. The "I Win. I Make Sure You Win. We All Win" attitude will likely be a challenge to cultivate but will be so worth the effort.

May this book provide the perfect initial resources to get you started on the journey. I hope that I have helped to equip you with the benefits of the vast learning I've achieved in an amazing twenty-plus-year journey of working with leaders and teams. In that time, I've wrestled with numerous complex topics related to strategy, ethics, values, virtues, coaching, consulting, human resources, interventions, etc., and have examined how these various subjects play out on both the local and global stage.

References

Ackermann, F., and Eden, C. (2012). *Making strategy: Mapping out strategic success.* Los Angeles, CA: SAGE Publications. Retrieved from Amazon.com.

Ball, M. (2015). "Is the most powerful conservative America losing his edge?" *The Atlantic*, (1).

Baldoni, J. (2014). *The Leader's Guide to Speaking with Presence: How to project confidence, conviction and authority.* New York, NY: American Management Association.

Beatty, K. (2010). "The Three Strengths of a True Strategic Leader." Forbes.com. Last accessed, 1 September 2013 at: http://www.forbes.com/2010/10/27/three-strengths-strategy-leadership-managing-ccl.html

Bolser, K. and Gosciej, R. (2015). "Millennials: Multi-Generational Leaders Staying Connected." *Journal of Practical Consulting.* 5(2). 1-9.

Caldwell, C. (2013). "Tomorrow's Global Leaders. People & Strategy," 36(3), 48-53. Caligiuri, P. (2012). *Cultural*

Agility: Building a Pipeline of Successful Global Professionals. Hoboken, NJ: Jossey-Bass.

Cameron, K.S. and Quinn, R.E. (2011). *Diagnosing and Changing Organizational Culture: Based on the Competing Values Framework.* 3rd Ed. Jossey-Bass: San Francisco, CA.

Center for Creative Leadership Handbook of Leadership Development. (2010). 3rd Edition. Eds. Velsor, E.V., McCauley, C. E. & Ruderman, M. N. San Francisco, CA: Wiley, Inc.

Corey, M. S., Corey, G., and Corey, C. (2010). *Groups: Process and Practice* (8th ed.). Belmont, CA: Brooks/ Cole.Cornish, E. (2007). Futuring: "The exploration of the future." Bethesda, MD: The Future Society.

Coach U. (2005). *The Coach U Personal and Corporate Coach Training Handbook.* Hoboken, NJ: John Wiley and Sons.

Denning, S. (2007). *The Secret Language of Leadership: How Leaders Inspire Action Through Narrative.* San Francisco, CA: Jossey-Bass.

DeSilva, D.A. (2004). *An introduction to the New Testament: Contexts, methods and ministry formation.* Downers Grove, IL: IVP Academic.

Dust, H. and Ziegert, J.C. (2012). "When and How Are Multiple Leaders Most Effective. It's Complex." *Industrial and Organizational Psychology: Perspectives on Science and Practice.* (5) 4. 421-424.

Fallows, J. (2015). "The tragedy of the American military." *The Atlantic*, (1). 72.

Fedler, K. (2006). *Exploring Christian Ethics: Biblical Foundations for Morality*. Westminster John Knox Press.

Fletcher, J. (2013). "Critical Habits of Mind: Exposing the Process of Development." *Liberal Education* (Winter 2013), 50-55.

Fine, A. (2010). *You Already Know How to Be Great: A Simple Way to Remove Interference and Unlock Your Greatest Potential*. Penguin Group: New York.

Fogg, N. P.; Harrington, P. E.; McMahon, B. T. (2012). "The Triumph of the Older Workers during the Great Recession: Implications for employers and disability policy." *Journal of Vocational Rehabilitation* (36). pp. 141-147.

Fontenot, S. F. (2015). "Politics and A Broken Promise: Why People Are Losing Their Physicians In Post-ACA America." *Physician Leadership Journal*, 2(1), 22-26.

Gourani, S. (April 25, 2019). "Leading Multiple Generations in Today's Workforce." *Forbes Magazine*. Last accessed: January 2, 2021 at: https://www.forbes.com/sites/soulaimagourani/2019/04/25/leading-multiple-generations-in-todays-workforce/?sh=71fcf0414636

Goleman, D. (2013). *Focus: The Hidden Driver of Excellence*. HarperCollins.

Hackman, M. Z. and Johnson, C. E. (2018). Leadership: A Communication Perspective (7th ed.). Long Grove, IL: Waveland Press.

Holinger, T. J. (2012). "Better by Design: Using Organizational Design for Competitive Advantage In the 21st Century." *Regent Global Business Review*, 5(2), 16-22.

Hultman, K. (2002). *Balancing Individual and Organizational Values: Walking the tightrope to success.* San Francisco, CA: Jossey-Bass / Pfeiffer.

Hunter, S.T., Cushenbury, L., Fairchild, J.(2012). "Partnerships In Leading for Innovation: A didactic model of collective leadership. Industrial and Organizational Psychology." *Industrial and Organizational Psychology: Perspectives on Science and Practice.* (5)4. 424- 428.

Hyatt, D. (2013). "Is America Losing Its Voice?" *American Diplomacy*, 1-7.

Javidan, M., and Bowen, D. (2015). "The Global Mindset: A New Source of Competitive Advantage." *Rotman Management*, 42-47.

Latham, J. R. (2014). "Leadership for Quality and Innovation. Challenges, Theories and a Framework for Future Research." *Quality Management Journal* (12) 1. pp. 10-15.

Levy, N. (2004). "Foucalt as Virtue Ethicist." *Foucalt Studies.* 1(1). pp. 20-31.

May, Thornton (2009). *The New Know: Innovation Powered by Analytics*. Hoboken, NJ: John Wiley & Sons.

Marsh, M., McCallum, N., Purcell, D. (2002) "Why Strategic Foresight?" Extract from "Strategic Foresight - The Power of Standing In The Future." Australia: Crown Content.

Michalko, M. (2006). *Thinkertoys: A Handbook of Creative Thinking Techniques*. (2nd Ed.) Berkley, CA: Ten Speed Press.

Paredes, D. (2015). "Data scientist: The job with negative unemployment rate." CIO, 1.

Patterson, K. (2012). *Crucial conversations: Tools for talking when stakes are high*. New York: McGraw-Hill, ca. 2012.

Pfeffer, J. and Sutton, R. (2000). *The Knowing-Doing Gap*. Boston: Harvard Business School Press.

Rahschulte, T. (2010). "Virtues of Leading Change." *The Journal of Virtues & Leadership*. (1) 1, pp. 15-24.

Ramsey, V. and Latting, J. A. (2005). "Typology of Intergroup Competencies." *Journal of Applied Behavior Science*. (41)3. pp. 265-284.

Schein, E. H. (2010). *Organizational Culture and Leadership*. 4th Eds. San Francisco, CA: Jossey-Bass.

Simpson, M. K. (2014). *Unlocking Potential: 7 Coaching Skills That Transform Individuals, Teams and Organizations*. Grand Haven, MI: Grand Harbor Press.

Slaughter, R. A. (1993, April). "Futures concepts." *Futures*, 25(3), 289-315.

Tung, K., and King, T. (2016). "Earning Diversity Dividends." *Mortgage Banking*, 76(7), 60.

Ulrich, D., Losey, M. R., and Miesinger, S. (2005). *The Future of Human Resource Management: 64 Thought Leaders Explore the Critical HR Issues of Today and Tomorrow*. Hoboken, N.J.: Wiley.

Whitmore, J. (2013). *Coaching for Performance* (4th Ed.): *GROWing Human Potential and Purpose*. Boston, MA: Gildan Media.

Wilson, W. (2013). "Coaching with a Global Mindset." *International Journal of Evidence Based Coaching & Mentoring*, 11(2), 33-52.

Wistrich, A.J., Ratchlinski, J. J., and Guthrie, C. (2015). "Heart Versus Head: Do judges follow the law or their feelings?" *Texas Law Review*. 93 pp. 855-923.

Xavier, S. (2005). "Are You at the Top of Your Game? Checklist for effective leaders." *Journal of Business Strategy*. (26)3. pp. 35-42.

Yoos ii, C. J. and Barker, J. R.(2008). "Covenons! We owe Are store to the company's soul..." *Journal of Human Values*, 14(2), 141-155.

ABOUT THE AUTHOR

Recently featured as one of the top 20 coaches in Washington, DC by *Influence Digest*, Dr. Shekinah "Ki" Magee is the successful Owner and Head Coach at Clear and Present Executive Coaching and Consulting Services, LLC where she works to support high performing teams in delivering superior service and partnering with customers to solve complex challenges.

This deep desire to help world-changing leaders and teams has led Ki on a journey of discovery, exploration, and learning, resulting in numerous awards and accolades, several degrees, and countless certifications. Most notable achievements include: Doctorate from Regent University, a Master's in Public Administration (Human Resources) a Master's in National Security from U.S. Naval War College, along with a bachelor's degree in Healthcare Administration.

Ki is a credentialled Profession Certified Coach with International Coach Federation, a Project Management Professional and Agile Certified Practitioner with the Project

Management Institute, a Lean Six Sigma Blackbelt, and a Certified Enterprise Agile Coach and Certified Agile Transformation Coach. Over many years and numerous client engagements, Ki has held the vision for leaders and teams as they embarked on the difficult and relentless work of improving performance, working together more seamlessly, and delighting customers with high commitment to service.

In this book, she shares the tools and practices she leverages when coaching, leading, facilitating, and instructing for the benefit of Executives, Entrepreneurs and Leaders working within Federal, Healthcare, Human Resources, and Technology Enterprises. This information has helped many leaders and their teams achieve higher order goals, and make better decisions, both in business and personally. This book was designed to support readers in realizing their team and organizational potential more fully, so they can win – on their own terms, and by their own design.

For More Information

Support Winning Teams in your organization!
Contact Ki at:
Phone: (240) 535-9683
E-mail: ki@kicanhelp.com

APPENDIX A:
A "THREE WIN" ONE-PAGE SUMMARY

The "Three Win" Philosophy

The purpose behind this workbook is to help talented individuals re-orient their thinking to become extremely impactful members of high performing teams –teams that excel at delivering high quality outcomes from within their organization. This has prompted the development of the Three Win Philosophy, based in the tenets:

1. I WIN.
2. I make sure YOU WIN.
3. That way, WE ALL WIN!!

In a Three Win world, people are not just responsible for their own personal success, but for the success of the other person. This philosophy, initially introduced while in casual conversation with co-workers, really resonates in that it can be used to outline clear and transparent approaches to figuring out how "we win" in organizations. It dismisses the old, problematic paradigm that someone must lose for others to win. It further dismisses the myth about "the greater good" that some managers use as an excuse to justify initiatives and actions that were not fully planned out or processed with enough intellectual rigor. Each of the three principles is supported by four supplemental concepts, outlined below:

1. **I Win.**
   a. Personal Development
   b. Coaching
   c. Values/Ethics
   d. Leadership Communication

2. **I Make Sure You Win.**
   a. Leader Development
   b. Partnering
   c. Talent Management
   d. Ethical Intervention/Consulting Design

3. **That Way, We All Win.**
   a. Strategic Leadership
   b. Organizational Design
   c. Leadership Analytics
   d. Global Consulting

A Gift from Ki....

Now that you have read **Winning Teams Workbook: Taking Teams from Average to Exceptional**, you are on your way to higher performance and unprecedented achievement, connectedness, and impact! Plus, your Customers, Teams, and entire Organization will obtain extraordinary benefits, as well.

You'll also receive the special bonus I created to add to your toolkit ... **The Winning Teams Field Guide**, which contains downloadable templates, assessments, and activity guides, along with additional instructions and my tips from various client implementations.

There's so much confusing information out there about how to take teams from average to exceptional and how to create, build, and sustain an organizational culture where these teams thrive and flourish. When you finish this book, you'll be armed with what you need to know to Win, make sure Others Win, so Everyone Wins!!!

While **The Winning Teams Field Guide** is offered for sale, as a special bonus, you can claim it for free here:

https://WinningTeamsWorkbook.com/guide

The sooner you know how to take teams from average to exceptional, the better your chances for improving your employees' and customers' experience and improving your entire organization.

I'm in your corner. Let me know if I can help further.

Here's to Winning Teams!

Best,

Shekinah "Ki" Magee

Made in the USA
Monee, IL
17 January 2022

89052088R00108